FRAGMENTS FRO
DARK

D0130531

1 MA

8 SEP 2022

CRIT

SWANSEA LIBRARIES

Libraries

WITHDRAWN

0001236717

Welsh Women Wr   *uge in Wales*

Sandscape after hours

Each print a journey
turns the beach into dreamtime.

They collide, converge
in silent riot of unmet strangers:

perhaps a supple body twisting,
flicking sand wishes to the wind

or two brains sticky in philosophy
slinging firm prints in terse lines

and there, a loner shuffles
an exotic weft into the mesh
and falters.

The sun glances severely, fairly, into every step,
pondering the pressure,

patterns of feet on sand,
each strand weaving dreamfibres into art

without start or end
just journeys

and
sweet sea havoc on the turn.

       Emily Hinshelwood

FRAGMENTS FROM THE DARK

**WOMEN WRITING
HOME AND SELF
IN WALES**

edited by Jeni Williams and Latéfa Guémar

2008

Welsh Women Writers and Women Seeking Refuge in Wales

© The Contributors, 2008

Front cover photograph © Emily Hinshelwood
Paintings reproduced on back cover and internal pages © Romisa Asadi

ISBN-13: 978-0-9545147-4-7

Published by Hafan Books

> c/o Tom Cheesman
> School of Arts
> Swansea University
> SA2 8PP
> Wales

www.hafan.org/orderform.htm

Enquiries: t.cheesman@swansea.ac.uk

Hafan Books is a non-profit voluntary project

All proceeds go to Swansea Bay Asylum Seekers Support Group and surplus is passed to sister charities working with refugees and asylum seekers in Wales

The following publishers' permissions are gratefully acknowledged: Ambit ('At a Happiness Symposium in Wales' from Nazand Begikhani, *Bells of Speech*, 2007); Gomer ('Autobiography 1' and 'Magda's Song' from Fiona Owen, *Going Gentle*, 2007; 'Beirdd y Mynydd Bach' from Stevie Krayer, *Questioning the Comet*, 2004); Salt ('Star Things' from Elizabeth Baines, *Balancing on the Edge of the World*, 2007); Seren ('Hieroglyph Moth' and 'My Dress Hangs There' from Pascale Petit, *The Treekeeper's Tale*, 2008; 'Veiled Woman' and 'Veiled Woman's Ghazal' from Carol Rumens, *Blind Spots*, 2008); and Unlabelled ('Where Are They Now' from Tracey Curtis, *If the Moon Could Talk*, 2004)

Published with the financial support of the Welsh Books Council

Printed in Llandysul by Gwasg Gomer

CONTENTS

Section 3: Travelling and Arriving

Section 4: Struggle

Section 5: From Silence to Voice

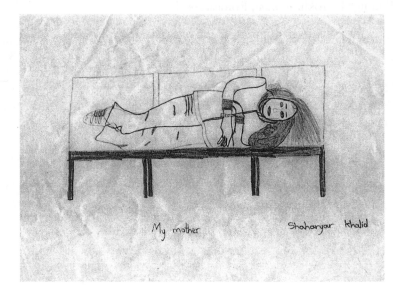

My mother   Shaharyar Khalid

Acknowledgments

Hafan Books is a voluntary project associated with Swansea Bay Asylum Seekers Support Group and Swansea Women's Asylum Seekers Support Group. The contributors and the editors have all donated their work and their time. Most copies will be distributed free of charge to asylum seekers. All proceeds from sales go to the support groups. Any surplus is distributed to our sister charity *Asylum Justice* (providing free legal advice) or to the *Welsh Refugee Council Hardship Fund* for destitute asylum seekers and other emergency cases.

For information about these charities, see the back page.

The print costs for this book have been met through a generous grant from *Cyngor Llyfrau Cymru* – the *Welsh Books Council*. We thank them humbly for their patience and their special dispensations. *Fragments from the Dark* will be launched on March 20, 2008 at the Dylan Thomas Centre, Swansea. This event is generously sponsored by the *City and County of Swansea*, the *Communities First Trust Fund*, and *Oxfam Cymru*.

Initial work towards *Fragments from the Dark* was undertaken by Andrew Hammond and Anahita Alikhani in early 2007. We are most grateful to them for assembling a substantial list of living women writers of Wales, or in Wales, and inviting each of them to contribute a short piece of writing on 'identity' and 'home'. The response was magnificent and moving. About fifty women writers sent in their work. We would have loved to publish everything. Fewer than half of these writers appear here, for reasons of space and – above all – balance with the work of refugee writers. We particularly want to thank those whose work does not appear here: their moral support is appreciated.

Our special thanks go to those who helped encourage and support women refugees in writing, helped produce testimonial statements, or helped with translating and other editorial work – among them Heaven Crawley, Sadhbh O'Dwyer, Sylvie Hoffmann, Sevdie Atashi and Carol Hancox – as well as to Emily Hinshelwood for permission to use her photograph of Tenby Sands; Catherine Fisher for permission to use 'Estuary Poems: V' from her collection *Altered States* (Seren, 1999); Romisa Asadi for her paintings; and Sherhayar and Shazaib Khalid for their drawings, reproduced on the facing and following pages.

Fragments from the Dark is dedicated to the memory of Kate D'Lima, and to all those who struggle to make the world a home, and to bear voices out of silence.

The place where I would like to live

Preface

> An exile is not just someone who has lost his home; it is someone who can't find another, can't think of another. Some no longer even know what home means.
>
> (André Aciman, 'Shadow Cities')

The photograph on the cover of this anthology was taken by the poet Emily Hinshelwood. It shows Tenby Sands, with the evening light slanting across the beach after everyone has left. The light picks out skeins of footprints which look like lines of longitude and latitude, like bird flights, like strange, looping writing. Traces of movement over the fluid border between sea and land, traces that will be washed away: a wonderful, perfect image for a collection of writings by women, for those seeking refuge in Wales and others who live and work here. The book's title evokes the sombre beauty of 'Fragments for the Dark', a poem by Elizabeth Jennings, but it also reflects the fragmentary nature of all anthologies. And yet 'Fragments *from* the Dark' suggests a more positive note: out of darkness comes something like hope, perhaps. Alongside some wonderful poems and stories from familiar Welsh writers, there are poems, stories and testimonies from asylum seekers and refugees.

André Aciman's musings on the significance of home provide a starting point. The exile, he says, lives in the 'key of loss'. Home is where you were born, grew up, where people knew you and you knew them. It is the original place of safety – if only in dream. To lose a home is to suffer a profound personal and psychological dislocation. Yet we are all exiled from the primary space of safety, to a greater or lesser extent. Our fluid, indeterminate selves are held together by fragments that shore up our ruin: bits of earlier selves, memories of lost family relations, places that haunt our dreams. The English have no word for the sense of existential exile, but the Welsh do: *hiraeth*, meaning an intense, spiritualised longing for a lost home. This word has transcended the language barrier, and now many English writers use it. Aciman's comments on exile evoke a universal experience of 'Fall' out of primary security. But for those who have been swept from their homes by tides of violence and terror, the loss of safety is accompanied by a terrifying loss of self. For refugees, *hiraeth* is magnified a hundred, a thousand fold. What the Egyptian-born Aciman describes as 'compulsory retrospection' deeply affects their sense of being: 'with their memories perpetually on overload, exiles see double, feel double, are double. When exiles see one place they're also seeing – or looking for – another behind it.'

Women, as traditional custodians of the home, have a very complex relation to its loss. And this is as true in Wales as elsewhere. Wherever they come from originally, the women writers in this anthology share urgent, interconnected concerns with home and self. The women seeking refuge find it more difficult to integrate into the public world, more difficult to speak out into an unfamiliar place and, of course, many find it far more difficult to express themselves in English. Just as disorientated by culture shock as refugee men, but in different ways, they also see double as they look back to their lost homes and families. It is unsurprising then, that, even when their English is not good, the lyric poem predominates in their writings. After all, in the words of Charles Simic, himself a refugee from the former Yugoslavia: 'a lyric poem is the voice of a single human being taking stock of his or her own existence.' In her poem 'Some Day', Afsaneh Firoozyar (from Iran) writes movingly of her sense of dislocation between two worlds, of being excluded from 'the sparrow's feast'. 'Dancing' by Mona Balbaki (from Lebanon) is an achingly beautiful reverie of dancing in the dark, and a riposte to the degrading mindlessness of those who knock menacingly on her door in the deep of night, or shout obscenities at her for wearing the hijab.

There are several reasons why we decided to focus this collection on the written expression of women. Men are more likely to have been educated and to have learnt English, and so they have dominated previous Hafan Books anthologies. We wanted to encourage and support some of the women we knew to develop their potential as writers. Another, equally important reason is that their individual, tender voices provide a vital antidote to the poisonous smears of the popular media, who routinely depict asylum seekers *en masse* as a faceless mob, usually male, single, aggressive and sponging – eating our swans and our donkeys, raping our women. The reality is that a high proportion of asylum seekers are struggling families, overwhelmingly headed by women. They seek their safety, their home, here. We don't often hear of their damaged selves, their anxiety and desperation, their fears and hopes for their children. And we don't usually hear about their suffering here, in the new place they cannot yet safely call home.

The anthology has been divided into five themed sections: 'Home and Homelessness', 'Looking Forward and Looking Back', 'Travelling and Arriving,' 'Struggle' and 'From Silence to Voice'. This thematic approach satisfyingly integrates resident and incoming writers. Those from Wales include professionals and amateurs, either born Welsh or settled here. Their writings sit side by side with testimonies, poems and stories about lost homes from women who have found themselves swept out by tides of violence and arrived, dazed with shock and loss, here in Wales (see in particular Nedjma X's 'Speaking Out' and Farzaneh Dadkhah's 'In Iran').

The writing of home is far more complicated than that of a simple place. Familiar relationships give the place of home its psychological importance. In this book, variously, an Iranian woman finds 'home' in helping others ('Working for Oxfam'), while Deborah Kay Davies's small son pronounces the freezing mountainside of their wintry picnic 'cosy', as he munches warm scones with his family ('Home'). For Jackie Aber (from Uganda) home is evoked through political fables. Other stories demonstrate a personal tenacity in rebuilding homes: from Parvin's testimony of release from an abusive husband into self-determination ('My Story'), to Maggie Harris's litany of developing homes ('Moving').

Most shocking for a public constantly fed lies about the supposed easy lives of asylum seekers, this anthology contains stories about the horror of enforced destitution here in Britain. The juxtaposition of Kera X's two narratives – 'My Home', looking back at her comfortable life in Ethiopia, and 'Homelessness', describing her present, desperate situation – is heartbreaking. Kera is a dignified professional woman who has always paid her way. Now in her late fifties, she finds herself constantly moving from house to house, too frightened to return to her homeland, and wholly dependent on demeaning charity, because she is neither allowed to work nor entitled to receive any kind of state benefit. Perian X gives a shocking account of being dragged away to a detention centre near London, revealing the devastating impact of this trauma on her young son ('Detention'). Such stories speak to our shared, deep need for a safe place where the self can blossom: but they do more. Fairytales and psychologists agree on the importance of the home to a stable sense of self, and here, to paraphrase Theodor Adorno, 'for a [wo]man who no longer has a homeland, writing becomes a place to live.'

Set against these refugee stories are other explorations of the idea of home. Catherine Merriman explores the confused mixture of fear, anger and pain felt by a mother as her son leaves home for university. Trezza Azzopardi depicts a husband's obsessive quest for a wife who has inexplicably vanished, and whose tantalising, fragmentary messages eventually drive him from his home. There are stories of 'incomers' and their homes, whether by Guyana-born Maggie Harris, by Elizabeth Baines, who meditates on the Jewish experience after the Second World War, or by Rhian Saadat, who travels through Spain seeking the roots of an instrument that is both Persian and Arabic, both Spanish and Gypsy, while her son – with his Welsh mother and Persian father – seeks his own home in music. Liz Morrison empathises with the anxiety of a refugee woman, as she waits in a British airport for arrival of the husband who represents everything about home. There are two original Arabic poems by Amani Omer Bakhiet Elawad, summoning up the joy and security of love, with their English translations, and an English translation of a poem of loss and return by Iran's most famous woman poet, Forough Farrokhzad.

This book testifies to the power of words to connect people across all cultures and the power of written expression in particular to open the world to itself. Catherine Fisher's poem on her Irish forebears expresses the perennial struggles of peoples fleeing their home, travelling, looking back, struggling and finally settling to a new life, a new home and self:

> I wonder
> how much time it took them to forget,
> learning a new country, new weather,
> resettling. How many generations
> to lose the flavour, mingle with the main,
> become diluted imperceptibly,
> word by unknown word; the children
> coming back with different accents, always
> the children first.
> Home known, home heard of,
> home receding into legend, and all the while
> unnoticed, this is home, and no-one says it
> till the moment's gone, the strange
> collective, calm decision taken.

'Estuary Poems: V', from *Altered States*

Section 1

HOME AND HOMELESSNESS

. . . this strange country . . .

Angela Hill-Jones

Fitting In

In 1984 I moved from my native Scotland to Wales; boy, was I the outsider. Twenty-three years later, living in Wales, married to a Welshman, teaching in a Welsh school, I still think of Glasgow as 'home'. Does this mean I haven't integrated, haven't become part of my local culture? Of course not. But it does raise the question of how deep integration can ever become, and how long the process can take.

These thoughts visit me now, as I consider the changes I have seen in Swansea over the years, and my ten years in Gors Community School in particular. The fabric of the school has changed dramatically; not only have the old Infant and Primary schools amalgamated, but the whole building has been modernised. Technology is everywhere; rows of PC monitors stand like mute sentries, testifying to the echoes of the past and the promise of the future. Environmentally, too, the school has changed. A new awareness of the need to understand and protect our world has emerged, involving staff, pupils, parents, and the wider community. Three times the school has gained the 'Green Flag' award, and we are currently applying for our fourth. This year the school won the Eco-Schools in Wales competition. As the school's Eco Co-ordinator, I am naturally proud of our achievements.

But it is in the area of diversity and multi-culturalism that I have seen the greatest changes. Ten years ago I taught in a class made up entirely of indigenous, white, Welsh children. Today around thirty percent of my class hail from Sierra Leone, the Lebanon, Saudi Arabia, Turkey, Iran, and Latvia. Along with the children come a whole network of parents, support workers, and interpreters. The experience in my class reflects the school as a whole and, indeed, the whole community.

In addition to the difficulties presented by having English as an Additional Language (EAL), we were concerned about how the incumbent children might react. We needn't have worried. Two elements surprised: the desire of the children of Gors to welcome and care for the new arrivals, and the speed with which the EAL children acquired a basic grasp of English. In no time the EAL children were scoring high marks in tests, tackling advanced reading books, and even, on occasion, out-scoring native English speakers.

I have noticed a deep commitment on the part of the EAL parents to education for their children. It is as if the difficulties that drove them to seek sanctuary in our country highlight the primacy of education in maximising opportunity. Even those parents who struggle with the language are deeply involved, always keen to discuss their children's development with me and the other teachers. And woe betide any child who misses their homework...

The EAL parents seem keen to develop a warm relationship with all the teachers, and frequently bring in samples of home cuisine for us to try. I'm becoming quite familiar with the savoury products of Iran, the Lebanon and Turkey. They are also extremely respectful of our religious differences. Last Christmas I had a card from a Saudi Arabian mother bearing the words, 'Happy Birthday To My Great Grandmother' – it has pride of place on my classroom display.

Geography lessons have really taken off. The new children have so much to offer, and it benefits the whole class to hear first-hand knowledge of a wide range of countries. The staff and children are dissuaded from enquiring about the reasons behind the seeking of asylum, but the odd snippet pops out. I have no idea of the pain and difficulties some of these families have faced.

The sense of Welsh identity within Britain is something the EAL children have embraced enthusiastically. What a joy to see their pride in wearing the Welsh national costume, daffodils and leeks on St David's Day. This cultural tolerance is reciprocated: the Welsh children encourage the Muslim children to bring in their prayer mats and explain all sorts of details of their beliefs.

Gors Community School has established links with a school in India. I and several other teachers have taught in India, and we have welcomed Indian teachers to Gors. The exploration of Christian, Hindu, Muslim, and even atheist beliefs, has played a major part in stimulating understanding and tolerance throughout the school.

So can these new arrivals fully integrate into Britain? Of course they can. But my experiences as an ex-pat Scot show me that, twenty years on, I'm still a Scot, albeit well integrated into Wales. It might take a few generations for our guests, with far greater cultural differences that I've had to cope with, to consider themselves British. But the children of Gors, the children of Wales, and the children of Britain owe it to them, and themselves, to at least try.

Dahlian Kirby

Aysha's Yard-Garden

Aysha woke to the sound of her brother coughing. These days, Aysha almost always woke up to the sound of her brother coughing. Her twin brother Mohammed. By now her older brothers would be awake and watching TV. Her baby brother Mustafa would be snuggled up beside her mother on a mattress in the tiny room without a door. Her father – well, nobody knew where he was. Or if they did, they weren't saying.

Aysha pushed back the Hundred and One Dalmatians duvet, a present from the nice lady at the church. She crawled over the bed towards the window, climbing carefully over her brother. Mohammed coughed some more. Aysha patted his head, the only bit of him exposed to the damp air of the bedroom. Then she rubbed a perfect circle in the middle of the condensation on the window and looked out. Her view was of the yard they shared with three other families. It was a long narrow yard, with a gate at the bottom that had come off from its hinges and was now propped shut with a long plank of rotting wood and a rusty supermarket trolley. Down the centre of the yard were the remains of an old pathway, yellow and broken like teeth in an ancient person, Aysha used to always think. Either side of the ragged toothy path were – but Aysha couldn't see, not without rubbing a larger hole, and that she couldn't allow herself. Couldn't, or wouldn't? The words held no separate meaning for her.

Aysha washed and dressed. She went into the living room of the flat, where, as she had expected, her three brothers were watching TV, all still in their sleeping bags to keep warm. In the tiny tiny kitchen Aysha put a pan of water on the cooker and took down some tea: Chinese tea, her mother's favourite. She opened a small glass jar and took out some ground cardamom seeds that she added to the tea. In her stomach there was a flutter of excitement. Today was the day!

Although all she wanted was to hurry down to the garden, Aysha took her time in the ice-cold kitchen. She made tea for herself, her mother and big brothers, warmed some milk for little Mustafa. She balanced all the cups on a tray from the nice lady in the church. The tray had pictures of little furry dogs on and at the bottom it said: 'A Present From – something beginning with B – Scotland'.

After delivering the cups of tea and the beaker of milk Aysha put on her jacket. It was massive, bright pink with many layers, again from the nice lady at the church. The big fat pink coat restricted Aysha's movements, but it kept her snug and cosy. Two new words she'd learned at school: SNUG and COSY. Aysha put on her gloves to make her fingers SNUG and COSY. She picked up her tea and went down the stairs. She went through Mrs Jama's kitchen. Mrs Jama nodded to her as she passed.

'Salaam aleikom,' said Mrs Jama as she fed her baby from herself.

'Salaam aleikom,' replied Aysha, not sure if you greeted a Somali person back with the same words. She put down her mug of fragrant tea for Mrs Jama to drink.

Aysha opened Mrs Jama's door. The door that opened on to the back yard. The yard that in her head Aysha called THE GARDEN. The garden was basking in the most incredible sunlight! Aysha stepped out into the garden and let her fat pink coat fall to the floor. As she took off her gloves, she heard a loud rap rap rap on the gate at the bottom of the yard.

Aysha dared herself to look up quickly. She saw the garden either side of the yellow ragged path – and yes! her flowers were still there! Aysha darted down the path and pulled the trolley away from the gate. Next she heaved at the plank of wood and pulled it away from the gate. She moved the gate sideways, today she had the strength of ten men, so it seemed. Into the garden came Amina, Layla, Fatima and Fatima's cousin whose name she never could remember. Shyly, behind Fatima's cousin, stood the new girl who wasn't a Muslim. She was from somewhere else, where skin was blacker and you didn't have to be a Muslim but you might be. New Girl didn't eat pork but did go and sing songs in the church where the nice lady who gave you things was. But New Girl was allowed in the gang, because really she was the same.

New Girl also didn't have a dad. New Girl was also an asylum seeker. New Girl also had ragged clothes and secret stories about bad people in the night. Aysha stood back and allowed all the gang to walk into the yard, where they stood on the path. Each gang member carried a red plastic bread tray, all of them 'found' by somebody's brother outside the bakery one night. On each tray each gang member had four or five plastic terracotta coloured plant pots. In each pot was a single white tulip.

At a signal from Aysha the gang began to unload their pots. Nobody spoke, but the feeling of excitement in the air was undeniable. Each girl seemed to know without being told where to place her pot. Aysha looked up and saw that Amina's sisters and cousin were arriving with their flowers; all arranged in white Styrofoam trays, found down a back alley by someone's brother. That's what brothers and boy cousins did, they found stuff and brought it home and gave it to you.

As the last girls arrived with the last flowers, the back door of Aysha's house opened and out spilled her mother, brothers and Auntie. They were followed by Mrs Jama and her baby, her husband and her sons. One son passed a wooden chair out to the other. The second son helped Mr Jama in to the chair. Mr Jama had been hurt by bad people in a country called Somalia in the night. Out of Mrs Jama's door came the gypsies from upstairs, followed by Yusuf and Ali from the top floor. The grownups all stood close to the door, surrounding Mr Jama in the wooden chair, as if he was a king and they his courtiers.

In from the bottom of the yard, through the open gateway, came the mothers of the gang, each with a bowl or plate of food. Aysha's mother hurried towards her daughter and couldn't help but exclaim: 'My daughter, what have we here?'

Aysha smiled shyly and took her mother's hands.

'This is a flower festival just for you. These are our friends. This is our Garden. Croeso.'

Aysha's mother looked across the filthy yard at the yellow ragged path. She looked at the wall that was crumbling, at the rusty trolley, at the sagging roof of the next house and the next house and the next. For a few moments there were no noises of traffic, this wasn't Cardiff. For a while the smell was of perfume. Transported from the decaying yard, Aysha's mother looked at the girls still placing flowers around her. And now she saw that each small girl was in blue, each girl wore a scarf. Each big sister was dressed as they would be back home. For now, Aysha's mother was safe and things were good.

Someone began to clap. Aysha's mother looked around her and saw that Mr Jama was crying and that sort of gave her permission to do the same. All thoughts of bad things in the night slid from the mind of Aysha's mother. The sun shone warm through her shalwar kameez. She thought she heard a bird sing. The girls in their scarves, the orderly row upon row of flowers, it was as if their yard had been turned into Paradise. Then Aysha's mother noticed that all of the girls were barefoot. She started to laugh.

Deborah Kay Davies

Home

I made a batch of scones;
flour falling,
the kitchen buttery.
Through misted windows
the winter garden stood
stiff, rimey, sage-green.

I was planning tea,
the Sunday papers,
a log fire, even Songs of Praise.
The children,
shut in all day,
clamoured for a picnic,
the mountain.

We parked the car
at a look-out point,
and impinged on the sheep
who chewed sideways
as we bent double,
like the trees,
up the track.

On the whistling summit
amongst smirking sheep-skulls
and flattened, scrubby stuff,
we found a slab of rock face
and squeezed into a semi-cave.
The sun was losing its balance
over the mountain's back.

I opened our basket
of floppy, warm scones,
poured tea from the flask.
We munched in the freezing air,
sheltered from the wind.
Pointing with his scone
at the shuddering grass
my little son said to his sister,
cosy, yes?

Elizabeth Baines

Home

Here is a tale the old woman told him:

I was newly married, she said. We had just moved to the cottage in Llanfair. I was twenty-six years old.

I was alone on a hot summer evening. I was cooking at the range. All of a suddenly I heard a strange sound. Like a bird, but not any bird I know, and I know them all: a clear, mellow, haunting sound, coming from just outside the door.

Like a signal.

I stood stock-still.

I wiped my hands on my pinny and crept quietly to the door.

I eased the door open.

The sound stopped.

I could see nothing. I stared at the garden wall where I thought the sound had been coming from: nothing but lichen baking in the sun.

Then a movement on the wall caught my eye, a beige flicker which I thought at first must be a lizard. It came into focus: a huge cricket, the biggest I'd ever seen, poised on the top of the wall.

It seemed to watch me a moment, and then it turned and hopped away down into the road.

I guessed where it had come from: the next cottage up the hill. My cousin had been living there with his wife and two children, but two months before his wife had died of consumption, and only two days ago he'd moved out, unable to bear being there alone. They'd always had crickets living in the warmth behind their stove, but for two days now the stove had been cold.

Next morning I knew that the cricket's song had indeed been a signal, but not to me. Overnight the crickets had moved out too, poured down the hill and under our door and through cracks we didn't know we had, and taken up residence behind our range.

And that was it. They were there ever after, you couldn't hang up anything made of silk to dry by the fire, they'd eat it right through. A curse we always called them. But I remember the stillness of the air that day, that lone defiant cricket watching and waiting, and that beautiful song, a song of hope and salvation, and I think of it as a blessing.

[Extract from an unpublished novel]

Imène Guémar

Being Happy

First, there is a bed, solid, wood.
A wardrobe, books … lots of books.
There is a TV, a video player.
Overhead there is a lampshade. Purple, shiny.
The clothes put away, tidy, neat.
There is a table, a chair, pictures on the walls.

It is calm, there is a view.
A nice view. It is pretty, clean.
It smells nice.

This is my room.
Cool, nice.
A private, useful space
A spacious space.
Calm.

Ingrid Bousquet

It's Nothing New

It rains
Over Swansea
This evening.
Each bead of water
Seals a second
On the clock.

Write something
Else
To erase
The first words
Which echo
In my head.

Ça n'a rien de nouveau

Il pleut sur Swansea
Ce soir-ci.
Les gouttes de pluie
Résonnent les secondes
Qui tombent
Sur mon horloge.

Ecrire quelque chose
D'autre
Pour effacer
Les premiers mots
Qui font écho
Dans ma tête.

Kera X

My Home

My country has a lovely climate. There are months of sunshine, it is open for every visitor. We have a very nice culture of hospitality; we show our love for everyone.

Where I live the town is big and busy. It is the main town of the southern region. There has been a lot of new building in the last ten years but the town was established many years back. I worked in a big hospital there for over thirty years. I worked in every department, in both in-patient and out-patient care. I like to help people.

My house was very big. In my country everyone lives according to their income, of middle class educated people. My house was very modern, everything was fully facilitated. I had a garden and flowers. I had everything I need. I miss all this. I miss my best friends, my family, every love from all those I know.

In general we have a good social life in my country. Nobody lives in his house alone. He will bring some relatives to live with him, or some other people who are not able to live alone. This is the love and experience that we have.

Some people in the country, their children come to the town and learn in the schools to get a good education. They don't mind if they give their children to someone good, so their children have a good schooling. This is how we help each other. Our relatives and our parents, we take them to our houses until they die. No one will be alone in his house. This is another kind of love we have. We don't drop them in one empty house.

In my house I had a girl from a family of my husband's relatives. She stayed with me and helped me in the house, and I helped her continue in her school. She is about fourteen now. When the school was closed she went to her parents to pass the time with them. In school time she stayed with us. Also in my house were my children. One is adopted, my nephew, my brother's son. We adopted him after my brother was killed [by government forces] and his wife escaped. The child is five and a half now. I have not heard about him since I came here.

[*Upset*] I don't want to say more about this… I don't want to talk about my husband. I want to talk about nice memories.

Our houses are all detached and on one level. We had a good house of mud brick, cemented and painted, with tiled floors, cool to walk on in the heat. The house is painted dark red, and inside a cream colour with white ceilings. It has three bedrooms. It is spacious. Enough for us all.

The area has lots of trees, but I don't have much garden, so I have only four fruit trees. I had flowers on the veranda and growing in the salon. In the salon I grew plants. *Harreg* has big green leaves, climbing up against the wall. *Kaffay abeba* is a small bush I had growing in the garden. It has variegated leaves, green and white, which you may cut and put in the salon. My veranda was full of flowers. I liked to take care of that. I had white roses and pink roses and small yellow roses.

I had many different flowers in the garden. I don't know all their names. You don't buy plants but share seeds and cuttings with friends and relatives. The pergola was covered with a plant growing with small bundles of flowers like grapes. Light purple, very sweet smelling. We liked to sit under the pergola on a long bench, to relax with coffee, in the shade in the hot sun.

We were near by the lake, and all around is small hills. We liked to sit on a veranda and look at all the big trees. Walking for six or seven minutes we came to the lake. There are lots of birds and fish. The birds are yellow, blue on the back, shining blue, golden birds, some big, some small. Many boys go fishing and bring the fish to sell in the town, carrying them in baskets, door to door. Small silver fish. There were many birds on the lake, some we call *daki-ey* have long long legs and neck. There are also some with dark wings and a red pouch under the bill. I have never tried to swim in that lake. There are crocodiles, and there is not a nice beach to sit and relax there. There are long grasses everywhere. We can sit on stones and relax, but we don't go in. For swimming, for the town people, there are two big hotels with pools in the hotel compound, and everyone goes there.

No birds sing at night. Early at six or five in the morning they sing. At seven in the evening it is dark. There is a long summer. In winter it rains sometimes, heavy rain, and then is not very cold. There will be a cloud, you expect rain, it is heavy and then it goes.

[The speaker was anxious after she had finished talking.] I am thinking about where I say that my brother was killed. Perhaps I will not say this. It is not nice. Perhaps the person who reads it will be upset, perhaps I will say just that he died.

Homelessness

To be homeless is very bad. I am just going from house to house. I am completely dependent. I don't have permission to work or to beg on the streets. I don't have money to go to Church. So how can I survive? How can I live going from house to house? And I'm afraid of being detained and deported.

I came to this country to save my life, but I am tortured and depressed here. I really understood how bad it is not to be in my country, so I prefer to go back to my country, and accept all the life-threatening challenges and ill-treatment – even death – among my family and friends.

In my case more weight was given by the Home Office to me speaking English than to my political activities. The Home Office thought, 'How could you speak fluently the language unless you stayed here a long time. You are a liar.' I tried to explain that learning in Ethiopia is in English, from junior to university. We learn our national language as one compulsory subject, but all other subjects are taught in English. But nobody accepts my explanation.

I am sorry to be accounted a liar. I am a nurse, and nursing is an international profession. They could have understood that my English is due to my education. In addition, I was blamed as if I had convinced the physician who diagnosed the damage to my autonomic nerve, after my ill-treatment in detention, so I felt very bad because the physician and I have professional ethics: nurses and physicians could never be solicited by someone. We have Guidance Ethics for all nations. So it was a pity for both of us to be accepted as liars.

Whenever I remember all the happiness I lost from my home and my beautiful country of certainty of sunshine, my tears flow all the time.

All my future is covered by darkness.

Interviews by Jeni Williams

Kimba Cate

The Real Garden

Me, my husband and our four children,
We took the bus out to Rhossili.
It was scary
But I wanted to see the garden.
A real garden, I was told,
A real garden.

I'm tired of shopping in Tesco.
I want to go back there.
The beans tasted delicious,
The babies slept in the buggy.

A real garden.
It was full of spiders,
Of plants, of flowers.
It reminded me of Africa.

I had wanted to see the garden
And I was happy.

[With Sylvie Hoffmann]

Maedeh Asadi

Freshness

In the big room
there is a little bed,
only a cot.
White sheets,
soft and clean.

There is an orange mobile.
It's dark but just a bit of the red curtain is open.
Everywhere is dark but just a bit of light is coming in.
A cupboard of ghosts.
A pigeon by the window
looking in.

Light moving through a child.
A child full of feelings in the darkness.
She cries, laughs…
she hears sounds, movements
through the window.

A room and a child.
And a mother, singing.
Her hug is warm
in the cold room.

The mother full of sadness.
The child is giggling now –
when the hunger comes
her mother gives her milk.

The pigeon by the window
looks in.

Pascale Petit

Hieroglyph Moth

When the white ermine wings
opened at night

like a book of frost
        smoking in the dark,

I understood the colours of vowels
painted on moth fur –

the black, red, saffron signs
of a new language.

Antennae grew from my forehead,
my tongue was restless in its chrysalis.

I felt lift-off
        as if my bones had melted.
I stepped out into the snow –

not even an exoskeleton to protect me
in this strange country.

My Dress Hangs There
after Frida Kahlo

The sky wants to wear my Mexican dress.
The towers of Manhattan want to wear her –
they feel naked with all that glass.

She was sewn with a needle of lightning.
Her lining is electric blue.
The sun and moon sleep in her pockets.

She hangs there homesick
     like a flag over the city,
without arms or legs
          but dancing over the roofs
with her American partners –
an abandoned toilet and trophy –

while my body lies on this gurney, pecked at
by the beaks of instruments
as an icy wind slices through.

Perian X

Detention

6 a.m. my door, one knock. It locked and my husband opened door and lots, twenty, police in five cars there. They told me, 'Relax, don't do anything, we deporting you your country. Get your clothes.' It 6 a.m., we in pyjamas. Children sleeping. I say, 'I want to change pyjamas.' Four women come with me when I change.

They told me and my husband, 'If you good we won't do anything to you, and if not... And then we put handcuffs on you.' I said, 'I want ring my solicitor.' They say no. They take my mobile and my husband's mobile. They say, 'You finished.' I say, 'How? I have Fresh Claim. I have no letter.'

The children get up quick. We have to go. In three hours they pack for me. They put stuff, clothes, in bags they brought. They took us to a prison. It was as if I killed someone. I upset and crying, 'For this – what I do?' It was nearly four hours travel to get there [Campsfield Detention Centre]. We went in a white prison van.

Amar, my baby, was crying. I said, 'I want to have him.' He was a year old. They said, 'No you can't.' Mahmoud [age 6] wanted to go to toilet. They said no. He wet himself. Mahmoud is crying all the way. No talking, just crying. He said, 'I don't want to go Turkey. I want stay here. My friends here. My school.'

Prison, big building, big walls with bars all around. If people come to visit they check your pockets, everything. At first, stay in waiting room to register us. Lots of people coming, they crying. They whisper the police hit them because they don't want to go.

Perian is very upset. Asked if she wants to stop she says no, just that she is remembering.

They give whole family one room. We go upstairs and after, I contact my solicitor. She say, 'I don't know why they come, I don't understand because you appealing.' The room very small room. Just two beds. They say we booked to go on flight next morning, 6 o'clock. I'm shocked, because I got problem in my country and I never thought this country treat you like this. And if they deport me my country, I haven't any chance with two children.

The next morning, 4 o'clock, they didn't come. 6 o'clock, they didn't come. 10 o'clock, they say they talk to solicitor. They say they deport my husband, not me. I say, 'We family, and he has problem in my country as well – maybe we never see him again.' I'm crying, 'Please don't deport my husband.' My solicitor managed to stop and they say, 'OK he stay.'

We had eight bags of luggage. They say, 'You have to go back Swansea.' They put the luggage on the path outside detention centre like we nothing, like animals.

My son he held his hands out in the air, 'Thank god we go back Swansea.'

We came back Swansea.

I went to see psychologist. [My friend] come with me. He said, 'You just shocked, you'll get better.' I say, 'I can't sleep, bad dreams.' He said, 'It normal.' Not give anything. After, my skin come bad – eczema, spots.

Perian's friend says: 'She never speak, just cry, cry, two weeks, three weeks. I shocked. She very active, busy, always joking. I shocked she change. I say, You strong, you have two children. Is not nice, but is life.'

Mahmoud is very bad now, very hyperactive. After we come back he just sit down crying, 'Mammy they coming again.' Now he wants to sleep with me. He get dreams, he shakes awake, he wets the bed. He seven now. Amar [age 2], sometimes he says he sees the police. If he's naughty I say, 'Police come,' he scared.

Sometimes I forget, but every morning I worry. 8 o'clock, 9 o'clock night, feel safe.

After that time I never sleep in that room, the children sleep with me.

...

We came by boat, very hard.

We only want be safe.

We came by boat, some women, their children died.

I don't want benefits. I just want be safe and work.

Interview by Jeni Williams

Stevie Krayer

Beirdd y Mynydd Bach

(Poets of the Little Mountain)

I stand at their monument and look down
over lake, ruins, farms, hills. I see beauty
but they saw neighbours. All the landscape
was named, known, intimate as the hand
in which they versified their *bro*.
Each hedge-thorn and fencepost recognised
and greeted them, every day the same
since before memory. All spoke
the same ancient tongue, born of tussling
together with the stubborn scrubland.

My foreign words skate lovingly across fields
smoothing away the detail as they pass.
I start acclimatising, taking root here.
Like a rhododendron in Snowdonia.

bro: region

An Evil Spell

Today Wales has been spirited away
by fog, like that Mabinogi story
where the king and queen awake
to nothingness – court, courtiers,
fields of barley, sheep, pigs, peasants,
steam from horses, smoke from hearths,
all uncreated as if genesis
had gone into reverse. Even
the nearest trees look insubstantial

As his olive groves that aren't
there any more must look
to a Palestinian farmer
stuck on the wrong side
of a teenaged checkpoint guard.

Sylvie Hoffmann and **Aimé Kongolo**

from White Goods

White Goods is inspired by the true story of a young man, a 'failed' yet 'non-removable' asylum seeker. A political dissident from a war-torn country in Africa, he has been made destitute and homeless, left to starve by the UK's current policies of discouragement and despair. He is denied refugee status, yet he cannot be deported. He is entitled to no state support or benefits, but also denied the right to support himself by working. He has endured this plight, in Swansea, since 2000 up to the present day.

He befriends and cares for an elderly woman, who puts him up. When she dies, she leaves him a massive new fridge-freezer, which brings him problems. Most people seem to be more interested in the fridge-freezer than in him.

A bed-sit room. Against one wall, a bed stripped bare. Two small cardboard boxes, packed. An open suitcase with a few clothes packed very neatly into it. A chair. A table. On the table, an open dictionary, some paper, a biro. By a wall-socket, on the floor, an electric kettle (just boiled) and three mugs. In the middle of the room, a large fridge-freezer in pristine condition, not plugged in.

Jamba polishes his fridge-freezer with great care. He opens an envelope on the table, takes out a couple of photos and blu-tacks them onto the door of the fridge-freezer. All the photos are of him.

Jamba: Helloooo!
        Just my face, up and down, with my little smile.
        I never had photos with my family.
        Like I never had one family.

He turns to speak to the audience.

        Hi, my name is Jamba, I have fled
        The boorish Bang! Bang! and
        Boom! in my country.
        Why the shooting? Why the killing?
        Indeed, why.
        Here, they sent me to Swansea.
        People greet me with a big smile:
        'Are you on holidays?'
        The solicitors, that's almost the first
        English word I learned,
        The solicitors say I'm
        'Cast in legal limbo'.

I feel cast in black rocks.

He starts boiling the kettle, gathers mugs and spoon. Opens the empty fridge, with a 'no milk' gesture. Slowly and deliberately he makes three cups of tea.

Yesterday, I went to this
Agency for some
Work.
The bloke, he was fine, then he says:
'Have you some proof of identity?'
I was so anxious, I said, 'Yeah!'
And I showed him this card we have to carry round.
This bloke (I like this word 'bloke')
He checks my face, fine, then I start laughing,
I slapped my head and I laughed so much
I nearly killed myself laughing,
As you say over here – kill.
The truth is I don't want to kill myself!
On this card, it says, in capital letters,
PROHIBITED FROM WORK, PAID OR UNPAID.
I quickly take my card back from him.
This bloke, he looks at me, he doesn't understand.
I left, still laughing.
This bloke, what is he supposed to do?

Stirring the three cups of tea.

Oh, sister, I'm hungry!
Nnno sugar, no sugar, – –

He slaps his head, realizing he has made three cups.

I'm going crazy, the old lady is dead,
Jamba, the old lady she is dead!

A knock on the door, expected. He opens it. A woman in her 50s enters, Mary, carrying a wrapped portion of fish and chips. She offers him the fish and chips.

No thanks, I've just eaten.

Mary sits on a box and they drink tea.

Mary: Nothing, nothing anywhere. Not even the Buddhist Centre. Yes, they do have rooms, they said, but No, cos you're not a Buddhist.

Jamba: That's not very Buddhist of them.

Mary: I'm truly sorry, Jamba. Let us pray.

She puts her hand on his arm. He gently disengages his arm and looks at her with big 'what the hell!' eyes.

Jamba: Such is life. Thank you, Mary. Sorry, but my head is hurting a bit. Last night I got a bit – what did they say? Plastered. Plastered?

He looks it up in the dictionary, laughs.

Afterwards I couldn't sleep. I tried the bed, I tried the floor. Maybe it's this war, war in my blood, war I was born with. Or maybe it's just that they won't let me work. So I never get tired. This slow slow death by starvation. If only I could sleep. I want to sleep, sleep, sleep! I want to sleep and die and yet I have to live…

Don't worry so much about me. I need to do things for myself now. When people help me too much, I become lazy. I can't rely on people. In my life those that I've loved, tend to die.

Mary: You can't go back to that telephone box by the station. Not you *and* the fridge!

Jamba: I don't want to live far from the fridge. It's all I've got.

Mary: You have to be practical! Sell it!

Jamba: I don't want to sell it, it's mine, it's a gift, I don't sell gifts. In my culture, when you sell a gift, it means you give it no value. I want to keep it. Besides, if I sell it for food, where do I chill my food? And it's a bloody good fridge, as you say over here. 'Bloody', I never understood why over here you say 'bloody good'. A funny saying that! In my country, all one breathes and all one sees is only pain, grief and blood upon human blood. Still… Where I rest my little head, it rests its little head!

As he finishes talking, Mary's phone rings, and she quietly answers, listens.

Mary: Thank you. *(To Jamba)* That's the Buddhist Centre. They've reconsidered, what with compassion and all that, they say they're willing to put you up, so long as you don't mind the fridge-freezer going into the communal kitchen, for the community.

Jamba slaps his forehead.

Jamba: Not again! Why does everyone want to separate me from my fridge?! The best gift I ever had. You know why? Because I can see myself, my face up and down, and I love it!

Mary: My offer still stands… You haven't got much time…

[Continues.]

Tiffany Atkinson

Philology

First, you write how heat
is like another body on your back:
you're losing *years* each day by way of minerals.
They teach you to drink Coke with salt in
for the sweating.
    Certain things seem close to home—
there's always someone on the hunt for something new
to say about the moon, and everyone keeps chickens,
but you can't get butter, never mind a European paper,
and the language is a minefield.
    Sixteen nouns
to hold the shapes explosion makes of civic space:
all derived from ancient artists' names. An Institute
which manages the rhetoric of pain. Its scholars
are exempt from service but (dear god)
they're thin. To reach its top floor you must climb
from brute hurt, through the drab, split-
levelled middle-management of trauma,
to the triple-glazed panopticon where dons
plot points of suffering so fine they're whistled
through closed lips. To hear that language
is to lean so closely in a man might kiss
or cut your throat.
    You find no word for *coast*,
for all that you smell salt at nightfall. And
you've lost your ID in a skirmish at the archives
so you'll have to trek inland. The letter
handed round for nineteen days says, underlined,
how [untranslatable] you miss the bloody seagulls,
strutting round *sans papiers*. And starling-storms,
above the shaky pier in Aberystwyth.

Section 2

LOOKING BACK AND LOOKING FORWARD

. . . from the top of the mountain . . .

Afsaneh Firoozyar

The Top of the Mountain

That spring everyone was going
to the top of the mountain.
Friends, families with children,
sisters and brothers.

It was hard to climb.
The mountain was very high.
But the exercise was good,
taking in the fresh air.

In winter it is thick with snow
but when spring comes it is green,
with earth, a little grass
and flowers everywhere.

The red of poppies,
yellow chrysanthemums,
blue galoria, white and pink magnolia
sweet-smelling narcissus.

On the top of the mountain everything is delicious.
After a long walk,
maybe three hours, or two,
sit, rest and eat.

From the top of the mountain you can look down,
over the whole town left far behind,
to dry rocks, a river
running between the mountains,
its waters transparent in the sun.

On the top of the mountain the smell is clean.
You leave the traffic of Teheran behind
and breathe pure air.
There are no exhaust fumes
on the top of the mountain.

This is my mother's land.
It is full of birds:
the small brown sparrow,

the yellow canary,
the green parrots with their red heads,
the harsh-voiced Kalok,
the white Kabutar.
All these call together in the spring.

*

One day in winter I went
with my daughter and my nephew
to the top of the mountain.
It was very cold but beautiful.
All the place was white because
the thick snows had come.

We walked a long time:
two hours, maybe three.
Me and my daughter
to the top of the mountain.

It was very clear and cold but
I was warm with walking.
Our hot breath like steam in the cold air.
The skin on my face, my nose, stinging.

We played with snowballs,
me and my daughter.

My nephew was a teenager,
always climbing, always excited, jumping,
calling, calling me to come with him.
And I shouting, shouting for him
to come away from danger.

On the top of the mountain
everything is precious
I miss my daughter now
But the spring will come.

Anahita Alikhani

Argue With a Foreigner

To learn the English language is difficult, but is nothing compared to learn how to think like an English.

My mission impossible is to think like an English speaker. After four years I still think in my way and then I translate it to English. Sometimes it is confusing for people and sometimes they can understand it, sometimes very simple things, like 'I wash my teeth', is odd for hearer, something like 'big like a Camel', 'stupid like a Donkey', 'harmless like a Sheep', 'skilful like a Lizard', or 'ugly like a Monkey'. Recently 'ugly like a Monkey' changed to 'ugly like George Bush'.

These are expressions which are used in daily conversation in my language and it is just a way to talk, not any intention to insult anybody. But here sometimes they cause a big argument.

Here are some mistakes or expressions that sometimes create big arguments!

A: Hello, how was your day?

B: Not good, I had a difficult day. I am very tired.

A: Tired? Why?

B: I couldn't sleep well!

A: Actually you slept like a Bear, and I heard you snore like a Giant!

B: WHAT?

A: I only mean to say, you slept well.

B: Do you want a coffee?

A: Yes.

B: Yes, please! You must say 'yes, please' in this country.

A: Yes, please!

B: Milk and sugar?

A: Yes, please.

B: Where is the milk?

A: In the wash-machine. Where do you keep milk?

B: I was just asking.

A: I was just answer!

A: Look at this kitchen! Dog is playing, Cat is dancing!!

B: What you mean, there's no cat or dog in here.

A: I know, but if there was it didn't make any different.

B: Oh you mean it's untidy. It's 'like a war zone', that's what we say.

A: When we say something is like a war zone, we mean it actually is a war zone... It is difficult for me to think like you; still I'm translating from my language.

B: You are living in Britain and you have to learn to talk like us!

A: You are like a grim Owl, nagging all the time.

A: Will you take the rubbish out?

B: No!

A: Will you go and buy bread? We've run out of bread.

B: No!

A: Why not?

B: It's not a man's job!

A: It is in Iran.

B: You're not living in Iran, you're living in Britain.

A: I know, I have to learn British way...

B: I'm bored here. Why don't you ever invite me out anywhere?

A: Because women shouldn't do that.

B: Why not?

A: We don't.

B: You're living in Wales – think like us. Of course they do.

A: You mean I should think like a British.

B: Absolutely.

A: You really want me to act like one?

B: Definitely yes.

A: From now on? Yeah...?

B: Yeah...

A: OK, you asked for this: Fuck off!

Catherine Merriman

The Beginning of Something

Kay and her son stood facing into the wind, looking out over the broad plain of the Usk Valley. They were taking a Saturday morning walk high on the side of the Blorenge Mountain.

'How's the head now?' Kay asked.

Alex frowned and said, 'Better.' His long dark hair was tied back into a pony tail, but several wisps had broken free and were pressed by the wind against his cheekbones. He still looked pale and hung over. Kay regarded him unsympathetically. She had had a late night too, lying awake rigid in her bed, waiting for his return from town. But, looking at him, she was nevertheless conscious of savouring the moment. Tomorrow he left Wales. Tomorrow his father would drive him to Colchester, and he would start life as an undergraduate.

She said this quite easily to herself. This morning, almost with relief.

Alex walked on, a yard or so in front of her. The track that circled the humping summit of the mountain was narrow, fringed with brown dead-head clumps of August-flowered heather.

The boy stopped again and fixed his eyes on the view. 'You won't ever move, will you?'

Kay drew level. 'Well. The house will be rather big for us now.'

'I mean from here. From this.' He nodded outwards.

Kay looked across the pastoral fields of the Usk floodplain, towards the Black Mountain horizon. Today, for once, where passing cloud shadow fell on dark upland bracken, the mountains did look black.

'You want to keep a stake in this, do you?'

Alex nodded. 'I can't imagine living where there aren't mountains. Be weird.'

'That's because you were born here,' Kay said. 'Mountains are like the sea. They imprint on the soul.'

Alex turned to look at her. 'You're not going to move house, are you? My room... You said... '

Kay smiled. 'I won't touch a thing.' But knew it wouldn't matter if she did. Alex just wanted the reassurance. He would never again live with them. Not as he did now, as a dependent child, living with his parents. Maddening, exhausting his parents.

'Did you enjoy yourself last night?' This was the first time she'd raised the subject. He'd said he'd be home by one, but hadn't returned till after three. All she asked of him, when he changed his plans, was a phone call. Anytime, however late. He knew she worried. That she stayed awake, and grew frantic with worry. But he hadn't phoned. And what a state he must have been in, when he finally had got back. All that coughing and retching in the bathroom.

Alex grunted at her. Kay managed to hold her tongue. Never mind. It had been a last evening out with his friends. A last celebration before the eighteen-year-olds scattered like seedcorn across the country. The last time, maybe, he would make her suffer like that. Ah, the media would have you believe that it was girls you worried about, but ask any parent of teenagers; of course it was the boys. Boys: who got thumped for strolling the wrong streets, or looking at someone the wrong way. Who spiked each other's beers, and held spirit-drinking competitions. Who showed off behind their driving wheels, egged on by their raucous, reckless, tanked-up friends.

The wind dropped. They had rounded a headland. On the skyline now to their left were hummocks of old workings, their outlines softened with bilberry and heather. Alex nodded at them and said, 'You used to tell us that trolls lived over there.'

Kay smiled. Alex was going a long way back. Digging up memories. Nostalgic already.

'And that underneath, King Arthur slept in his cave. With all his warriors.'

'Any myth you like. On your very doorstep.'

Alex halted. Impulsively he flung himself down on to the heather. The sun was hot here. A strong, yellow, late-September sun.

He rolled on to his stomach, so his face was half buried in the heather. 'Laura won't be coming over to Essex with Dad and me tomorrow. She told me last night.'

'Oh?' Kay found a dry flat stone and perched herself on it.

Alex turned his face to her. 'She thinks... we ought to cool things. With, you know. Her in York, and me –'

Kay sighed. A big soft motherly organ opened within her, and hurt for him. How dare Laura. Even if the girl didn't love him – as she clearly didn't – and might be right to do this, if she didn't.

'I'm so sorry,' she said. Poor Alex. Such a romantic, emotional, whole-hearted boy.

Alex said, 'Yeah,' and sighed too. Then screwed his eyes up. 'I suppose when I get to Essex they'll expect me to play rugby, shag sheep, and say boyo a lot. Shit.'

Kay smiled. 'Will you expect all the local girls to be called Sharon and wear white stilettos?'

'Ha ha.'

'Well then. It's the same for everyone.'

'I suppose I feel Welsh.'

'You can be Welsh, English, anything you like.'

Alex swivelled to face her. 'What was it like for you and Dad then? When you came here first? Being English. Didn't you feel kind of alien?'

Kay shook her head. 'Didn't cross our minds.' She laughed. 'The English don't think about being English. Like men don't think about maleness, or white people about whiteness. It was just an adventure.'

She brushed her hand over a particularly dense, springy clump of heather, pushing at its resilience. 'D'you remember that story? About the farmer who sat up here to smoke his pipe? Put his baccy down and it fell into what he thought was a rabbit hole. But he couldn't reach it, so he went home and got a torch. And when he shone it into the hole he saw that he was looking down into a vast chamber, a cathedral cave hollowed out in the limestone.'

Alex was silent. Then said, 'Why d'you tell me that?' and turned onto his back.

The words *we must protect the children* flickered across Kay's mind. But we mustn't baby them either, she thought. Why had that story occurred to her? Just after she had refused to identify with his sense that he was moving to a foreign land. Was she being cruel? Telling him a story that suggested that even the ground beneath his feet, the ground of his homeland, might not be solid or safe.

'I suppose,' said Alex, 'That it'll be weird for you too, now, with only Dad in the house.'

'Oh,' said Kay lightly. 'Women thrive on empty nests. We take up Open University courses and toy boys.' She wondered why she felt so flippant. Because, underneath, she was still angry with him, she supposed. Because she could face, quite easily today, the idea of life here without him.

Alex's profile tipped to the sky. 'This is kind of the end, though, isn't it?'

'The beginning, darling,' Kay corrected him. 'Surely.'

Alex exhaled a slow, punctured sigh. 'I'm gonna really miss Laura.' His voice had a thin, insecure edge to it.

Oh dear, Kay thought. He's scared. But only a weak compassion stirred in her. A small, duty ache. And it dimmed beside another, much less charitable emotion, with a self-righteous voice that hissed: so it's your turn now, Alex, out there on your own. Now you'll start to understand.

She looked at her watch. It was a fair walk back to the car. She got up.

Alex said, with his arm across his eyes, 'I don't want any lunch. I'll walk home.'

She frowned down at him. 'It'll take you hours.'

'I feel like it,' said Alex.

Kay shrugged. 'If you're sure.'

She returned to the mountain car park for the car and drove home.

'Alex is walking back,' she told her husband Ed, who was laying the table in the kitchen. 'He's hung over and miserable. Laura won't be going with you tomorrow, by the way. She dumped him last night.'

Ed's face twisted. 'Dumped him?'

'Yes. Bit cruel, doing it on his last day.'

Ed groaned. 'Maybe better than a Dear John letter in a few weeks. You can feel pretty low, in that first term.'

Kay realized he was right. 'I think maybe you should have gone on the walk with him. He's scared. I think I just made him worse.'

They had a soup and cheese lunch. She kept some back for Alex's return – not till about four, she guessed. Then went outside to garden.

At five she returned to the kitchen and stared at the cooker clock. It said the same as her wrist watch had outside. She found Ed, who was kneeling on the back seat of his car in the drive, rewiring the stereo speakers.

'Is Alex back?'

'Haven't seen him.'

'Right.' Kay went back into the house and upstairs to the landing. She opened Alex's bedroom door. In the middle of the room was a pile of cardboard boxes, a portable CD player, an electric kettle, and an open, nearly full suitcase.

She nodded to herself. It was the beginning of something. She went downstairs, and back outside.

She built a bonfire at the bottom of the lawn. When the flames were well-established she fed them with small logs, and then tossed on a wheel-barrow load of perennial weeks. The fire pumped out thick grey smoke. Or was it steam? Whatever, it was smoke-signal stuff. She pulled a sour face at it. A home fire, burning.

A capricious gust of wind blew the dense grey plume into her face. Eyes streaming, she jabbed the pitchfork into the ground and stumbled back to the garden path. She almost bumped into Ed.

'No Alex yet?' She blotted her eyes with her sleeve.

Ed shook his head. She followed him into the kitchen. She didn't want to look at the clock, because clock-watching never produced missing children, but couldn't help herself. Nearly six. Ed was looking at her oddly.

'I got a face-full of smoke,' she explained, trying to smile.

'He'll be back,' Ed said.

Kay wasn't sure if he meant this afternoon, or from Colchester.

'I know,' she murmured.

Ed turned to wash his hands in the sink. Kay felt her heart start to thud, a slow, building drumbeat. A familiar tattoo. Oh God, she thought, last night was meant to be the end of this. Is he punishing me, for thinking that, and welcoming it?

'I can't start supper until he's back,' she said. 'Where the hell is he?'

'Alex is hopeless with time,' Ed said soothingly.

'Yes. But I wish Laura hadn't –' Now the subject was broached, her fear was rising. 'He's so emotional… and impulsive…'

'And selfish and unthinking,' said Ed. 'And not a hysteric. He's fine, you know he is.'

Did she? She saw Alex's face, pale and tragic. His arm, flung across his eyes. Heard his thin boy's voice crack. There were old quarries on the side of the mountain, with sheer unfenced cliffs. Further down, low-walled viaducts over deep gorges. Emotionally too, boys were more vulnerable than girls. The boy in the next street had cut his wrists when his girlfriend dumped him. It was only luck that he had been found, and saved. And he hadn't had the prospect of leaving home the next day, of having to start a new life somewhere foreign and frightening, on top of his grief.

She gave up and let panic overwhelm her. Though she despised herself for it. But she would panic for him, experience the loathsome, exhausting feelings, one more time. She poured herself a whisky. Refused to start the evening meal, or do anything that might take her mind off her son's absence. Contemplated, as the slow seconds ticked by, at what moment she would ring the police. Or mountain rescue. Or

Laura. Sunset was at seven. It would be torchlight black by eight. As usual, she managed to hold in her mind the two incompatible convictions: that something terrible had happened to her son – because why else wasn't he here? – and that it hadn't, but that unless she worried for him, it surely would. Because that was when disaster struck, when you pooh-poohed the risks, and let your defences down.

By seven she was vindictive with rage and anxiety. She couldn't sit, or stand still, or occupy a static space at all. She tried to infect Ed, unsuccessfully; his resistance, as usual, was high. He cared, he insisted, but didn't believe that worrying helped. To Kay, a cruel, infuriating view, suggesting that beliefs and superstitions were optional, that she could spare herself this ordeal, if she so chose.

But Ed did at least, today, acknowledge her anxiety. He looked concerned. He said, 'D'you want me to go and search for him?'

She said, 'Yes, I do. I do,' and burst into tears. And then made the silent admission, feeling forced into it by her invisible, reproachful, missing son: that yes, life without him would be a catastrophe. That she would miss him, terribly.

And while Ed was comforting her, and trying to put on a coat at the same time, they heard footsteps outside. And then a cough, unmistakeably Alex's.

Deborah Kay Davies

Auntie's Place

Back to the billowing garden
washed in a gaudy, wall-flower delirium,
where the raspberry oozes and bursts
in a course of brightest blood
to track and mimic
warm, blue veins in a thin, white wrist,
sole witness to a trespass.
Back to the sneezy geranium,
and the cat lying drugged
in its own hot pool of black and violet fur.

The enclosing stones drone with heat.
Heavy-headed roses
droop and shriek for moisture.
Blundering butterflies flap
through a sweet syrup of perfume.
Drowsily they knock and dust
the blossom-knots of the wilting holly-hocks,
candied and scrunched now,
brittle as crepe paper.

A slow-motion, carpet-slippered wait
for small, sugared tomatoes,
nestling in leaves of damp mint,
and glistening fruit in fluted amber dishes
with wafer-thin bread for the juice.
And angel-cakes that float
on crackling, white cloth-clouds
in tongue-melting swathes
of palest lemon and pink.

The walnut piano after tea
and always the clotted lilac, deathly sweet,
that throws itself
at knuckles knobbed and stiff
but able still to ease out
those boned, long-skirted tunes,
while the evening faces in their silver frames
smile down.

From open, mothy window
the woods are piles of dusky pillows,
wafting and tumbling one on the other.
Only I know the secret of that bare summit
where the devil built his wicked heap of stones
with seared and scaley hands.
The piano is silent; the frames are blank.
There is no-one left but me
to walk the little paths and lean to dodge
the swaying swags of dew-hung phlox.

Elin ap Hywel

The Cost of Children

The chalk from your bones,
their future a powdery trail
on the cinder path in front of you.

The salt of your tears.
Perhaps, if you're lucky,
a drop to spice your stew
perhaps a dark lake that floods its borders
to lap at your windows and doors.

Your patience, your wisdom (if you have it), your prudence
will flutter down, bright painted cards
knaves grimacing, queens sneering as they fan and fall.

They will come in the night, enchanted
and steal the sheep's wool of your warm ambitions.
In the morning it hangs, glittering cobwebs
of dreams on the posts of their beds.

The sweat of your brow, the juice of you
they will drink it in with their mother's milk,
their faces and hair will shine with it
while you lie in the corner, cored
your pips squeaking, your flesh turning brown

– and yes, the bottom of your heart,
it goes without saying they will cost you that:
the battered leather bucket
that goes down again, again into the red well
and rises, always, brimming clear to the rim.

Farzaneh Dadkhah

All My Love
for Ali

Every day I wake up with the sun
I am having good things
I listen to the sound of music
Music I imagine

Dancing, jumping, singing
Dancing jumping singing

I open the window
The view is red green blue pink

The man in my dreams comes in close
I hope so
I hope so

This man has lots of love
I hope so
I hope so

He brings lots of love
I hope so
I hope so

Gwyneth Lewis

Amgueddfa Genedlaethol y Glannau, Abertawe
17ed o Hydref, 2005

Beth sy'n dyst i'r trawsnewidwyr?
Tirlun. Priodas gwres a mwyn
yn creu man cyfarfod. Pridd yn troi'n gadwyn,

yna'n drafnidiaeth. Morwr ar long
yn paentio pluen i'w danfon at ei fam.
Tanwyr yn moli ar allor y fflam,

yn creu ymherodraeth. Beth yw cof
y corff am ei lafur? Cryd
cymalau, cromfach cefn mewn gwely clyd,

a chelfyddyd pethau – swn
dur ar ledr yn hogi min
ar rasal fy nhad, sy'n estyn ei en

er mwyn iddo eillio. Amser yn ffrwydro
fel metel mewn ffwrnais. Beth yw pris
cyfoeth? Bod yn brentis

i broses. Beth yw braint
diwydiant? Na chollir gronyn
o egni. A'r galon yw'r gloyn.

National Waterfront Museum, Swansea
17 October, 2005

What's witness to the transformers?
Landscape. The marriage of mineral and heat
creates a place for people to meet. Soil is a chain,

then transportation. A sailor at sea
paints a feather to send it home.
Firemen worship at the altar of flame,

forging an empire. What memory
do bodies hold of labour? Aches
and pains, a back's bracket in a snug bed,

the art of objects – the sound
of steel on leather honing the blade
on my father's cut-throat; he stretches his chin

to begin his shaving. Time explodes,
red-hot, from a furnace. What's the price
of wealth? Being apprenticed

to process. And the privilege
of industry? That not one quantum
of energy's lost. And the heart is the ember.

Jackie Aber

Two Fables from Uganda

The Story of Mr Leopard and Mr Hyena

Once upon a time there lived a Mr Hyena and a Mr Leopard. The two were very good friends and they did many things together. One day, Mr Hyena came up with the idea that they should go swimming. The two friends went to the lake and had a nice time. 'It was good, wasn't it?' said Mr Hyena. 'I think we should take our mothers to a swimming competition tomorrow. I want to see whose mum swims faster and better.' 'My mum is scared of water,' said Mr Leopard. 'Don't worry,' said Mr Hyena. 'We'll wrap them up so they won't see where they're going'. 'OK,' said Mr Leopard.

The next morning, Mr Leopard wrapped his mum up and took her to the lakeside. But Mr Hyena wrapped up a pounding mortar,[1] instead. 'Let's throw them in the water and see whose mother swims fastest,' said Mr Hyena. The two of them counted one, two, three, then threw the two bundles into the water.

Mr Leopard's mum went deep in the water but Mr Hyena's mum was swimming on the top of the water. 'You see! My mum is the best. I didn't know that my mum was so good at swimming!' said Mr Hyena. Mr Leopard was very sad that his mum had disappeared in the water. 'Let's go home now, my mum will come back after crossing the lake,' said Mr Hyena. 'I think my mum is dead,' said Mr Leopard. He was very sad but Mr Hyena was very happy.

When Mr Leopard reached home, there was nobody to cook food for him. He decided to go to Mr Hyena's house. When he got there he found Mr Hyena very happy at home with his mum. 'Can I stay with you?' asked Mr Leopard. 'No way,' said Mr Hyena. 'But why?' asked Mr Leopard. 'Because you are stupid, and I can't be friends with a stupid creature like you. You killed your own mother,' said Mr Hyena. 'But we both threw our mothers in the water!' said Mr Leopard. 'I didn't,' said the hyena. 'I saw you with my two eyes,' said the leopard. 'You think I am stupid like you?' asked Mr Hyena. 'I threw in the pounding mortar.'

Mr Leopard was very angry with his friend. 'I will kill you!' he shouted. 'You tricked me!' Mr Hyena and his mum took off, singing: 'Stupid Mr

---

[1] *A pounding mortar is traditionally used to grind grain in Uganda.*

Leopard killed his mum when he threw her in the water! Clever Mr Hyena only threw the pounding mortar!'

This story tells us that we should listen to a friend's ideas but not follow them all. Choose some, but leave some out, or else you will end up like Mr Leopard.

The Story of the Lion, the Fox and the Ass

Once upon a time there lived three animals: an ass, a fox and a lion. They decided to hunt together and to share equally whatever they caught.

Their first prey was a fine fat stag. The ass divided it into three equal parts and gave each animal his share. The fox was pleased with his portion, but the lion was very angry. 'I am much bigger than you,' he said, 'and much angrier. I should have the largest share.' So he fell upon the poor ass and killed him and ate him up.

Then the lion turned to the fox and asked him to divide the stag. The fox picked out the fattest and choicest morsels for the lion and chose only the thin, small pieces for himself. With this the lion was very pleased. 'You have done well. This is how it should be. Who taught you to share out meat in this way?' The fox answered, 'It was from an ass that I learnt my lesson, and it was the foolishness of my master that taught me wisdom.'

Jo Mazelis

Asylum Seeker

Cunningly disguised as human beings,
we step upon the displaced planet.
Our only difference
to your unsuspecting senses
might be a whiff
of unfamiliar jasmine oil
or the faintest suspicion of a broken
atom of cracked coriander seed
lodged beneath a finger nail.
That, and a darting shadow
scorched on the eye
of someone, somewhere
fled from,
and someone, somewhere
still loved.
And somewhere itself –
a place ever longed for
where birds and stones
and rivers know our names
and we, theirs.

Meryam Fotohe

My Father's House

I remember when I was a girl,
before I was married
My father had a garden.

But my father has died
and the garden lives only in my mind,
magic and bright.

That garden has a carpet of tiles,
pale green and patterned white.
Slowly, in the early morning, the birds sing there.

For a short time before the hot sun comes,
the birds sing like angels in the trees,
and the trees move softly in the breeze.

Under each leaf, a small drop of water.
A pond lies under a tree of flowers
its red petals fall to the water's surface.

The small orange fish are happy there,
swimming round tiny flowers that are
pink and covered with pollen dust.

Spring has arrived there, come from far away.
Winter was very cold and the people suffered.
The time was long and the spring almost too late.

Now the flowers smell good.
There are no clouds.
There are two white chairs in the corner.

Now my son and daughter,
active and busy, are playing in that garden.
And even the stones smile.

My father's garden:
such pity, such sadness,
it is gone.

Mona Balbaki

The Seashore

I remember one time
I walked by the seashore
early in the morning.

I heard the birds sing
The small green hassan,
bright with purple and orange,
called from the ekdenya trees.

I heard the soft waves,
one by one slowly breaking,
slowly breaking on the smooth sand.

I sat and played with the sand,
writing memories, listening to the
birds round the houses and rocks.
The salty taste of the sea.

The cold breeze made me shiver a little
then I drank warm coffee, watching the sea.

Thinking, my mind goes far away,
floating, with my memories, over the sand.

Dancing

We dance
in the dark.

Dancing in the moonlight
and walking out under the fresh trees
in fresh air.

There are different kinds of flowers.
Tiny flowers, white, yellow, red.
The shadow of the leaves dark in the dark.
It's spring time.
The smell of jasmine, nerjes.

Dancing in the motion of the music,
feel the sound and warmth of it.
When you are alone
you feel the warmth of music

The sound of nature.
the creatures,
the sound of birds, the bulbul.

And the colour of the dark sky
which takes you to the end
and makes you move
step by step.

The taste of mint in this lovely dark night,
the taste of sweet in this slow motion music.
See all these wonderful things,
feel it never ends.

Monika Okoro

Margate, Kent

Margate, Kent
It was a quiet place.
Not much to do.

We were always doing nothing.
Only breakfast, lunch, dinner.
Nothing else to do.

So lonely, alone,
scared no one liked me,
crying every night.

A single room.
Brown wardrobe.
White small sink, small tv.

Small windows, no curtains.
The backs of buildings outside.
Old reddish factories, half dirty, half clean.

I was lonely, alone,
Crying every night,
Thinking about my family.

It was summer, very hot, when I came.
Children everywhere.
And no one could speak English.

I thought no one liked me.
I thought being an asylum was very horrible.
I thought it could not be accepted.

I felt abandoned, full of fear.
The baby moving inside me:
The only thing that made me happy.

I missed my family.
I missed the life I used to have.
I missed everything about my home.

In Margate, dirty carpets.
Everything grey.
The smell of stale cigarettes everywhere

I thought of the smells of home,
Of the food, the garden, my bedroom,
Of feeling relaxed.

Back home my mom cooked maize meal, cabbage, spinach.
In Margate they gave us potatoes, kebabs and pizza
Every night.

In Margate I felt abandoned, full of fear.
In Margate we were always
Doing nothing.

Sadhbh O'Dwyer

An Acceptable Ethnicity

Like most nice girls from rural Ireland I left it as soon as I could. By the time I was 21 I was living in Paris and working as an English teacher, an ice-cream seller, a dog-walker and a tour guide. Despite all these jobs I had very little money; no doubt due to hanging out in the dodgy Hungarian-Irish bar near Saint Sulpice. One day I went to visit my friends who lived in far-away Villepinte near the airport. With no money for the RER fare I jumped the barriers. On the train I was unlucky enough to run into a ticket controller. I explained in my most charming French that I was a lost tourist from Ireland, a country with more cows than trains. The controller laughed and let me off the ticket fare, saying, 'Ireland is a very beautiful country and you like to drink too.' (Hurrah for alcoholic Ireland!) On my return journey I jumped the barriers again, thinking, 'You can't possibly meet a ticket controller twice in one day.' Of course, I met the same ticket controller who thought it all hilariously funny, and mercifully didn't fine me. Then he moved on to the African woman sitting opposite me. She had three young children with her and no ticket. There wasn't time for her to give a quirky anecdote about life in Senegal as she and the kids were kicked off the train at the next station.

Since moving to Wales, I think about that Senegalese woman more and more. Here, people tell me all the time how great it is to be Irish. My midwife has told me that 'Irish people are always happy' and the woman in Sweetmans says that 'the Irish and the Welsh are the same, we're all Celts.' (The bakery is perhaps not the place to point out that the Irish are a mongrel breed and that the same could be said for the Welsh.) I'm commended on the loveliness of my accent and it seems that Irish accents are suddenly deemed sexy. Occasionally I meet morons who put on a funny 'Oirish' voices and dance leprechaun jigs, and people do ask my advice on potatoes, but these are the exception rather than the rule. So why do I feel uncomfortable with compliments on being Irish? It's because it feels like the flip-side of racism.

To be Irish in Wales means to be different – but not that different. People are more likely to ask me where I come from than to chat to my African friends about their home. Africa is too Other whereas Ireland is just across the water. The Irish sell themselves as the 'happy-go-lucky' folk of Europe – we are very good at marketing, we even sold our national day to Guinness. Ten years ago I would have been the one to be searched at Heathrow airport (reddish hair, Irish language passport); now Muslim women are the suspects. I suppose I should feel lucky, I'm part of a 'cool' ethnicity. I don't have the BNP attacking my house and there are no more 'no dogs, no blacks, no Irish' signs. However, I can't shake that feeling that to be 'acceptably Irish' is somewhat fickle and rather mistaken. I think of that Senegalese woman and I feel ashamed.

Tracey Curtis

Where Are They Now?

I remember when I was small
All the colours of my home and all of the smells and sounds
Where are they now?
I remember all my family
Aunts and uncles, cousins close to me, we would play for hours
Where are they now?

I remember when we said goodbye
We had to leave our toys and clothes behind
I remember how it made me cry
I'd wish for yesterday and close my eyes

I remember my new home was grey
I longed to feel the sunshine on my face but it rained all day
Where am I now?
I remember feeling so alone
We had to come here to be safe, I know, but I wanted home
Where am I now?

I remember feeling scared some days
When people told us we should go away
At night I'd listen to my father cry
I'd wish for morning and I'd close my eyes

I remember how I made new friends
I learned their language and I played their games and I found my smile
Where I am now
I remember hearing we could stay
Being allowed to work and pay our way and find a home
Where I am now

I remember when I had my child
How I'd do anything to make her smile
To keep her safe and always by my side
I think of yesterday and close my eyes

Section 3

TRAVELLING AND ARRIVING

. . . nothing stays the same . . .

Amani Omer Bakhiet Elawad

اليك ارتحل
قوافلا تسارع الخطي
تسابق الزمن

اليك ارتحل
عوالماً لأجلك
تعانق الهوي تفارق الشجن

اليك ارتحل
روائعاً بحبك
توقع الغناء
تصطفي رحاب صدرك

اليك ارتحل
جوانحاً لقربك
تداعب الصباح
تحتمي بنور صدرك

اليك ارتحل
سواحلاً مشوقه
تغازل السحاب
تشتهي مياه بحرك

اليك ارتحل
اليك ارتحل

I Journey Towards You

I journey towards you
joining the fastest caravan,
seeking to overtake time.

I journey towards you.
I will give you new worlds
with the recovery of love, the loss of suffering.

I journey towards you.
Miracles will be inspired by your love,
marvellous songs will choose
the wide space of your breast to be their home.

I journey towards you
to be close to you,
to be cradled by wings in the morning of love,
to shelter in the light of your dawn.

I journey towards you.
The passionate beaches
ache to touch the clouds.
They crave the waters of your ocean.

I journey towards you.
I journey towards you.

Translated by Amani Elawad and Jeni Williams

Fiona Owen

Autobiography 1

September 1964/March 2003

When I was five,
my father drove us
from Portsmouth to Qatar
in his new Jaguar

and what I remember
was the drive across the desert of Iraq
and a Land Rover full of the Sheikh's men

pulling us out of the sand
again and again,

returning for us,
feeding us,
and leading us
to Baghdad.

Tonight, in Wales,
the TV screen shows that place ablaze
as shock-and-awe destruction
sinks in
    and I can only think
of that bright sun on my young head
and the feeling I couldn't then name
of being part of a circle in the sand, sharing rice.

A Wet Wales Sunday

On a wet Wales Sunday, the family car
whines up a one in eight slip of tar
into cloud. A cardigan of sheep unravels
when the father gets impatient and beeps the horn.
Whatever he'd imagined, it wasn't this
and the car windows are steaming up.
The children in the back know to be silent,
the daughter praying her mother won't snap
under the strain of I-told-you-so's.

Spume and vernacular, wind-scream wipers not coping,
the village emerges out of the rain and rock, the chapel
leaning into the road like a big hand saying Stop.

The father winds down his window to a man
in a grey overcoat, whose sharp nose drips rain.
I'm looking for a property called Bryn-something, says the father.
He can't pronounce it, but compensates with a Valleys pastiche
which makes the daughter clench her toes, her brothers
elbow each other and the mother, to smother
her own urge to laugh, cough the family cough.

On the M6 home, the father's certain
the place has prospects could fetch double the price
with work and barn conversion, the land in good nick
and planning permission later, in the bottom field

and on and on he goes while the daughter knows
her mother's mind has wound up like a car window
against rain and gales, her wipers working against the plan
to sell up and move to Wales.

Kate D'Lima

Branwen

'Nothing stays the same,' said the old servant woman, Fatima, looking up from the spices she was grinding. Branwen, the young woman she addressed, said nothing and kept her head down, kneading the dough for the puris. She let her hair fall down to cover her face but Fatima could see the swelling below Branwen's eye and the brown and purple bruise the cook had dealt her. 'Even if you wanted it to,' Fatima persisted, pointing a gnarled finger at her, 'nothing stays the same.'

Branwen shaped the dough into little balls and ignored Fatima, who sighed and shook her head, muttered something to herself, then went back to making the masalas that filled the kitchen with their scents. Branwen dusted the flour from her hands on her sari and picked up a handful of dried fruit from a pot. She went out into the yard where the morning sun was already fierce, and sat beside the cage of a myna bird with a drooping wing. She opened the cage door and the bird hopped out onto the kitchen step, bobbing its head and chattering in welcome with a varied repertoire of squawks, chirps, clicks and whistles. It let her stroke its neck and hopped onto her shoulder, where it made soft chattering sounds and nibbled gently at her ear.

She sat on the step in the shade and listened to the music of the bird's sounds. It tried to peel open Branwen's fingers with its yellow bill to release the fruit, but she kept her fingers tight.

'Talk to me first,' she said, teasing it. Branwen only spoke in English to the bird; Bangla was the sole language in the kitchen.

'Talk to me first,' the bird repeated, then laughed like Branwen, fluffed its feathers and said, 'The cook beats Branwen. Tell the ravens. Go and tell Bran.' It hopped about on strong yellow legs, squawking and clicking, pleased with its vocal display. It did an encore then flew back to Branwen's hand, making crooning sounds.

Branwen thought of the starlings back home in Wales that pecked crumbs from the back yard of their restaurant. The bright yellow tablecloths were shaken outside, scattering pieces of poppadums, rice and nan. Immediately the starlings would descend and strut around with their inky star-flecked bellies. She remembered that her own name meant 'white raven' in Welsh. Her brother's name was Bran and together they had made up a secret language as children and believed it was the speech of the birds.

'Tell Bran what's become of me,' she said to the myna bird as she opened her hand and gave it the fruit. She held the bird close to her lips, stroked its dark feathers and pulled at the injured wing that was now healing well. She whispered again and again, 'Tell Bran; tell Bran.' She imagined the bird passing on the message to other birds throughout Bangladesh, who would pass it on to seagulls, who would take word to the shores of Britain. From there the message would travel to Swansea Bay, where the ravens and starlings would find Bran and tell of the cruel treatment to his sister. She stood up and threw her arm out, making a wish and releasing the bird to the sky. It flew up to the tamarind tree where the monkeys chattered a warning, then allowed it to settle.

She closed her eyes and tried to imagine her home in Swansea where Bran could be found. Instead of the dry field ahead of her with a peasant in a loin cloth driving a bullock with a ploughshare, she saw the streets of her childhood, where she had been happy. She remembered the Little India of St Helens Road with its sari shops and Asian supermarkets selling mangoes, bhindis, spices and huge fish in freezers. Although mangoes and guavas dropped from the trees here in India, she still longed to see them in boxes outside shops on chewing gum stained pavements. All nationalities shopped along the street, weaving between each other with bunches of coriander, second-hand books or bags of bananas. 'Swansea the sweet witch,' she and Bran named it, and she now longed for its contrasts and rich squalor. She thought about her family and the restaurant, and of her brothers and half brothers. But most of all she longed to see her brother Bran, who had given her away to Ahmed, her husband, to honour their late father's wish that she marry him and return to Bangladesh.

Bran and Branwen were born in Wales and given Welsh names from the Mabinogion by their mother who believed in the power of myths. They learned Welsh in school, spoke English with friends and Bangla at home. But to each other they spoke their secret raven language, until they went to school. At first, sitting at their school desks, they whispered their own language behind cupped hands, until the teacher moved them to separate desks to help them integrate.

Branwen's life had stayed the same for three years now, despite Fatima's insistence that change was inevitable. Ahmed had instructed his head cook and butcher to beat Branwen each day, and had banished her to the kitchen where she worked slavishly from morning till night and then slept on the bare earth in a hut. The reasons he outwardly gave were trivial. He claimed that Branwen's half brother had insulted him when he visited Swansea. But Ahmed deeply mistrusted Branwen's previous experiences and a way of life so different to his own culture. The discovery of a small dark raven tattooed on her hip was enough for Ahmed to imagine that she'd brought shame on his family.

It was close to the monsoon season some months later when Fatima found Branwen feeding another myna bird and talking to it in English. The air was heavy and even the birds in the trees fell silent. Only the incessant sound of sitar and tablas came from the crackling loudspeakers in the village. Frogs were beginning to collect on the dry cracked earth, waiting for the rain that was imminent. Fatima sat on the kitchen wall opposite Branwen, wiping the sweat from her brow. She shook her head from side to side, looking at the bruises on the young woman's arms.

'I told you nothing stays the same,' she said, pointing a turmeric-stained finger at the darkening sky. 'My family have seen signs.'

Branwen looked into the worn, toothless face of Fatima and shrugged. 'Nothing's changed for me,' she said in Bangla, and continued to stroke the bird that squawked and then imitated the croaking of the frogs.

Ahmed had told the servants that Branwen was forbidden to talk to anyone outside of the kitchen or to send or receive a letter. Their punishment would be instant dismissal if he was disobeyed or if Branwen strayed further than the small back yard. This was the reason for the mistrust and fear between Fatima and Branwen. Yet the old woman wanted to help Branwen, if she could still keep the job she depended upon. If it was her daughter, she thought, she would help her escape this lonely existence of talking in English to birds.

'My brothers have told me of strange sights in Dhaka,' Fatima whispered, looking fearfully around her. 'The pink sky of dawn is filled with swarms of birds – myna birds fill the air with shrieks and strange babbling. They turn the sky back to night, then suddenly leave like gusts of wind.'

Branwen's face broke into the first real smile Fatima had seen.

'My brother is coming,' she shouted and ran, laughing, through the house and down the path to the street, crying, 'Bran is coming!'

Fatima went after her, calling her back. But Ahmed had come to see what the noise was about. 'What is this?' Ahmed shouted at Fatima and grabbed her by the shoulders, shaking her.

'She says Bran is coming,' Fatima said quietly to Ahmed.

Ahmed ran over to Branwen who was leaning on the gate, looking up and down the street. He turned her around to look at him and their eyes met for the first time in over three years. Ahmed saw that her face was bruised but that she was still strong; perhaps stronger than him. Branwen saw the fear in him. Despite the darkness of his eyes, she saw more panic than anger and a weakness of spirit that may have come from stubborn remorse. Instantly she knew she was free.

'I need money and my passport,' she said, and pushed past him to go into the house and the rooms they had once shared together. As she packed a case, she looked out at Ahmed who still stood at the gate. He seemed thin and broken and already part of the past. She knew he wouldn't stop her when she left for the station.

Kimba Cate

Forgiveness

Life is difficult in war-affected areas especially for children and women. When I remember what happened to me and my children I can't hold back the tears. All this happened when my husband joined the rebellion to fight the dictatorial regime of Mr Museveni, the president of Uganda.

Myself and my children were not aware of my husband's involvement with the rebel activities. We were arrested but managed to escape from captivity and things turned against us. Soldiers attacked our house and searched for my husband and information related to rebel activities. When they failed to find what they were looking for, they started beating me and my children in order to reveal the whereabouts of my husband and information. Due to the way they treated us that night, we were forced to locate to another part of the country, leaving all our belongings including our beautiful farm. In a way, I will never forget this until my death. We settled in another part of the country. The second time they attacked our home we didn't know how they came to find us. I think this time they came to kill us because when they broke into the house they told us to remove our clothes and started beating us. The shamba man [*servant*] who was living at the boys' quarters heard the screaming and then the soldiers started chasing him. We decided to run away and in the confusion we managed to escape, scattered in the banana plantation. This time we decided not to live in Uganda anymore. Things were not so easy as we didn't have the money to pay for the journey. I gave part of our land to a friend who arranged our journey via Rwanda to the UK.

We started looking for my husband using the address which we used to write to him when he arrived here in the UK. When we arrived we were happy because he was not expecting us. It was as if we were dreaming. We cried tears of joy, he begged me to forgive him for what happened to me and the children. We accepted his apology. This happiness was short-lived however as the Home Office refused to allow us to stay with him. He fought tooth and nail but not until the Refugee Arrival Project stepped in to help us could we succeed. Eventually we were allowed to live together. We had just started building our lives together when a dispersal notice came. We were scared at first and we thought, 'Maybe they are taking us away in Swansea.' Things were not easy until we got to know the Swansea Bay Asylum Seekers Support Group which has changed our lives and we now feel like a part of the community. We are valued here and there is respect for the law unlike in Uganda. We managed to get an allotment which at least helps to remind us of our life in Uganda.

Even though I now feel like a valued member of the community, I think back to everything I left in Uganda – all the things that took me and my husband time to work for. These are now abandoned and unattended. I can't hold back the tears. I would like to thank Swansea Bay Asylum Seekers Support Group and the community of Swansea. Finally, I request the British Government and other first-world countries to stop financing dictatorial regimes, not just in Uganda but around the whole world.

Liz Morrison

Arrivals

I need to find somewhere to sit, the child is heavy and my legs ache. I head towards a cafeteria selling overpriced, cheap coffee. It is as busy as the rest of the airport and I look around for any empty chair, even if I have to drag it away to the periphery.

Anywhere I could rest while I wait.

But no one has a free chair, even as I go about asking, no one volunteers their own seat. So I am left to lean against a concrete pillar and people watch while I stare at the arrivals board.

The flight was due in an hour ago but it is delayed. It left in bad weather.

I have been in other airports, but not this one. This one is new to me but somehow familiar. The plastic faces of the staff and the blanket single-mindedness is the same.

I dare to hope to see someone I know, which is impossible.

The man I am waiting to meet is the only familiar face I will see, and have seen since I arrived here myself.

I have missed so much about him, the sound of his voice, the smell of his hair, the shadow cast by his frame. What will he say when he sees me? Have I changed? Is my face older, paler? Am I thinner? What of our child? How much he has grown? Or will he see none of this through his tears?

I will not tell him I slept here last night. Trying to find rest in a dark corner where the lights had been switched off. The chairs were useless with their metal armrests. I chose the floor and let my little one have my coat as a blanket. We stayed there until dawn broke, with the sound of cleaning carts and luggage buggies. I lost most of my luggage at the last airport, what I have now I keep to hand in a tatty black bag which is worn from all the travelling around.

We have done much travelling since we arrived here; me, my child and my little black bag. We have slept on many floors, some beds. Jeopardising others as they provide shelter. Getting to know them took some time; you cannot stay with people you do not even know exist. Between arriving here and meeting those people was a very dark time. Yet I always held my loved one in my heart. Wondering if he could know I was thinking of him. Sending him my love in thoughts and dreams. Willing him to know of me in that very moment. I have missed his company most. Touches and kisses are less than equals to the friendship and company of the one you love. Yet the first thing you do when you have not seen one you love for so long is to hold them and kiss them. But now all I want to hear is his laughter, his conversation, what he thinks and what he has to say. To know him through his thoughts and hopes. So he can remind me why we fell in love.

He is unaware that I do not have a home to take him to once he arrives. The other people that the plane has emptied itself of will leave here for plush hotel suites, parents' safety, their own sanctuary or a friend's hospitality. Long after they have gone we will still be standing here, lost in another world. When they sit down to their first plate of hot food, or rest their head on an unfamiliar soft pillow, my husband and I will still be here.

I had no friend to tell how excited I am, to discuss what clothes I will wear and what time he is due, how much I have missed him and how I will cook him his favourite meal. My clothes are the same ones I wore as he waved me off. He is due whenever the plane lands. I have missed him more than words can ever tell and the only meal I can provide will have to wait.

Will he have changed? Will the scarring be less now? Will he still be struggling with change, hesitant to challenges which would have once seen him rise to combat? He was beaten, both physically and emotionally in the attack. He said they would come for me next and that I must leave. He said that it was because he loved me that I must go. He had no time to explain, he would not let me get a cold, damp cloth to wipe off the dried blood forming in the creases around his nose and mouth. He was limping... will he still be limping now? How much damage did they do?

I wept for him as he rushed me and our son into a neighbour's car. The infant screaming in distress as the wheels spun on the patch of ground outside our house. I did not turn to watch the man I love disappear behind me. I held my baby and cried into his hair. My tears rolling down his forehead to mingle with his as the driver threw instructions to me over his shoulder. He was telling me times, places, giving me instructions with no way for me to write them down. I repeated as much as I could to myself, over and over, fearing I would forget them. I did. But I remembered London airport, and the date and time when I would get there and the name of the person who would meet me. I did not know there was more than one airport in London. The person who should have been there must have been at one of the other airports, they were not waiting for me when I landed.

I did not even get to kiss him goodbye.

When I got here, with the baby silent and finally tired from screaming I asked for assistance. For help. I was taken to an office. I waited until the person was available and that is when the forms began. So many forms and all wanting English. My father, a doctor, had met many Englishmen so had learnt a little and taught a willing daughter everything he knew. It was not enough. Not enough for forms.

My husband is a clever man. He speaks no English but is known at home as a man of knowledge. He is involved with writing, and with politics, and with journalists. He is regarded as an honest man who holds integrity and wisdom in his community. I am a good match for him; I come from a good family, a doctor's family. My husband and I live in a good area, in a nice house with nice things. We have friends who are also known for their upstanding position in our society, yet here, here, we mean nothing.

The distorted announcements are broadcast overhead and the arrivals board changes, giving different information from the disembodied voice. The flight has landed, but it seems, no one knows where.

I cannot go to where he will be as I do not know. Where are we supposed to go? My child has woken and is hungry. I cannot stop to feed him as I have to wait for the board to tell me where my husband is. The man I love and want to see more than anything else in the world. I took him for granted each day, coming home needing to be clothed and fed. Talking to him as if we had all the time in the world to spend together, now I feel sick at my ignorance, how we should have held each moment as precious. I have longed to see him again, to tell him that I will never take him for granted again, that I will not use precious time to tell him that he needs new shirts or that his hair needs to be kept tidier.

Now he is here somewhere, and just like when something inside responds to a child's cry, something inside me knows he is here, somewhere. In this maze of busy, faceless people, down some corridor, behind some desk my man is waiting for me and I am not there. What if he goes to the same kind of office where they ask unanswerable questions and insist on speaking a foreign language and cannot find a translator and treat you as if you have the brains of some unfortunate?

The child is crying louder now and I can hardly hear my own thoughts.

There are two gate options. One must be right. I cannot stay here, child bouncing on my hip, black bag swinging crazily from my shoulder, I run and run and run to the gate number stated on the board. But when I get there it is closed; a man says there was a mistake, go to the other gate. Out of breath now with a child confused as well as hungry, broadcasting its unhappiness loudly, we run again, struggling desperately. If I can just find my man things will be ok. We will be safe. He will find us shelter and food and we will have love again.

There are many people at the gate and as I push my way through to the front I see my husband. Looking as lost and bewildered as I must have been and I shout his name louder than all the other people can shout and the tears spring to my eyes and I shout again and again and again until I am shouting and crying together and his arms are around me and his jumper is absorbing my tears. And I know that this is over, and just begun and I know that I no longer care.

Maggie Harris

Moving

When my hand strayed and found the lump in my throat I wasn't surprised. When they found a name for it I recognised it. Somewhere on my body a physical manifestation had to occur.

It's been thirty-seven years now. When I think of what that number really means I can't comprehend it. Just like I can't comprehend a voice travelling invisibly from mobile phone to mobile phone, or that people aren't really in the telly.

I continually get a shock when I look in the mirror. The person that stares back at me isn't really me. She started to change only recently, some four years ago or so. The whole thing was sneaky, sometimes I'd catch a glimpse, something around the eyes or the cheeks. Not getting the full picture until a photograph my sister Mary had taken offered itself up out of the pack. The worst shock was that those full pouty lips have quite quite gone. The ones the boys used to go wild for, and the white girls used to tease. Funny how lips can disappear, I wonder where they went.

When Daddy appeared behind me through the dressing-table mirror I had jumped. My hand put the tube down and I pressed my lips together just like I'd seen Mummy do. He stood there and looked at me, then shook his head.

'Since when have you been wearing lipstick?' he asked, as if half-afraid of the answer. I relaxed, the tone surprised me. 'Oh ages,' I said flippantly, 'ages.'

It was a different story in 1992. There was no fear in my daughter's eyes. Neither myself, her step-dad, her real dad nor the school could deny her the right to wear full-on face make-up. We were grateful enough if she went to school.

The river my dad worked on sails through me at night. I had thought it was the menopause that was keeping me awake but that was just another word, like thyroid. She enters like a charmed snake immersing me in her bauxite eyes.

'Here, take the paddle,' Wallace says, 'don't be afraid.' And as long as I keep to the creeks I feel safe. Wallace guides me round the mangroves singing a Demerara folk song whose tune I can still remember but only the words of the chorus remain: '... you will know that you are down in Demerara, Demerara, you will know that you are down in Demerara...'

You can see the Berbice river from our gallery window. 'Mummy, you know that Daddy family was from Africa?' 'What nonsense you talking, girl, you Daddy born up Berbice River.' 'Before that,' I sigh. 'Don't let you Aunty hear you talking such foolishness,' she snaps.

I love my boyfriend so much I don't want to leave him. 'What you want to go Englan for?' he says. We are wrapped around each other on the front porch. From downstairs in the yard you can hear the crickets and the crapauds fighting for the night. 'You know I don't like that place. Is America I going man.'

'You wanted to come,' my mother says thirty-four years later as we drive her to Lake Bala to see a church some priest made out of a stable. 'Besides with your Daddy dead who was going to look out for us? At least my brother was here.'

'So what kind of accent is that?' the English boy called Martin said, his voice shouting above the music. He looks just like those boys we saw in films like *To Sir With Love*. 'No, not Ghana,' I say. 'Guyana'.

'Where is that exactly?' the woman with the little boy says. We are at mums and toddlers at the St Lawrence Church hall and my arms are feeling long and awkward. My little girl runs off into the toy corner, the little boy chases her, laughing.

This is a nice street, I realise. Those who migrate from one country to another do not immediately read what are extremely important signs. 'Oh no,' my fiancé had said, discarding one of the houses I had chosen to look at. 'That's not a good area at all.' And under his guidance we had found the right one. And I push my new baby smoothly past the black and white thirties semis and the old lady cutting her roses in her garden smiles and peeps in the pram cooing.

The young mum from mums and toddlers seems surprised to see me as I wait on her garden path with the pushchair. 'You did say pop round anytime ...?'

'Come up girl! Come up!' Mrs d'Andrade has dropped in, climbing up the front steps hot from the sun and my mother sends us for ice and lemonade and the best glasses. They sit in the gallery and laugh and laugh and me and Magreta get out the Christmas dolly and strip her completely naked.

'No way you're getting this house,' my ex-husband says.

I jump awake and don't know where I am. My eyes frantically search the wall for clues. Am I at home in New Amsterdam, is it that dream of me waking, the imprint of a soft kiss on my cheek? Is it the time of the earth tremor in 1966 when everybody in the whole country was wide wake and I was not except for Mummy saying 'You want me to wake her?' Wake her. Wake her.
Am I on that sofa my uncle put me to sleep on in 1971, for three whole months, some girlfriend's because, times are hard in England y'know, your Mummy don't realise. Or am I walking the cold November streets in Harrow-on-the-hill returning from evening art classes and the street is so long and all the houses look the same and save for motor cars gliding there is not a soul to be seen and my ears uncurl into the night sky listening out for Aunty Lucille shouting at her children or Daddy's pickup truck in the drive or my boyfriend Shaheed's whispers please don't leave me I love you and my mouth is dry for the remembered texture of roti, my nostrils running in the cold, crying for the smell of garlic pork and pepperpot.

No it must be the Ramsgate house, that house where I brought my newborn and my ginger cat Gertrude runs pell mell out of the house at this strange new piercing mewing and doesn't return for four days.
It looks like that house, it smells like that house, it is an orderly house with magnolia on the walls as I don't know anything about decorating yet and when I begin to experiment I will reach for William Morris palm tree print and it will be years down the line when I will read John Agard's poem about palm trees, years of holding babies years of unskilled factory work shop work cycling walking down streets that never get familiar no matter how often I walk them, and I am never sure

if I am pronouncing the words right, the way I say things have the propensity to amuse so I reach for unfinished education and amongst the open minds of students Africa whispers to me through music insinuates such movement in my ankle bones and hips I am possessed and at the barbecue the mums from mums and toddlers laugh and look at me strangely as I dance to Salif Keita calling it that strange music and it must be these student types and the streets beneath me move

the walls change. Is this the bedroom in Broadstairs? I don't recognise this pallid paint, wasn't I done with magnolia? No! The house in Broadstairs where I bought my third girl child home, Aimée, the loved one. That house with the cobalt blue dining-room, the peach front-room, the emerald green bedrooms, the bright yellow bathroom and my kitchen, my kitchen, my brand new worked-for kitchen, bought with prize money for writing, writing, writing.

My eyes spring open awake and I realise that none of those places exist for me anymore, my restless feet and fevered dreams have cast me back into limbo; rented walls and dreams of Wales, another beginning, another belonging slipping through my fingers like the crumbed earth we are forced to toss into my father's grave so long ago so long ago long long ago 1969.

Meryam Fotohe

Working for Oxfam

I am Meryam. I was born in Iran. My family and I moved to the UK in April 2005 so we have lived here nearly three years. When I lived in my country I worked in a charity shop because I love people. I feel for poor people and suffering people too and I want to help them.

At first, when I came to Wales, I did not work in a charity shop and I missed it. But then I came to a drop-in meeting at the church and someone told me to go to the Oxfam shop. My friend went to the manager and told him about me and then the manager rang me and asked me to come to work in the bookshop. I was so pleased. I started there more than three months ago and I now go once a week.

Some weeks ago the manager invited me, with the group from Swansea, to the national Oxfam meeting in Aberystwyth. I had not been to Aberystwyth before and I liked the journey. It was very nice, very beautiful. We drove through villages and the country and I chatted with my friend. The meeting was about Oxfam's work. I liked it because Oxfam works with everyone in the world, not just British or Europeans but everyone. Most of the Welsh volunteers were there, they were very friendly. I liked all of them, they are very good people, very kind, educated, sympathetic people.

After the meeting finished my group went by the sea and had coffee, tea and chips and we were happy, laughing and chatting. We enjoyed ourselves. We were seven people on a trip. We went on the pier.

I can write in English because I went to school in Iran before the revolution when the Shah had made English compulsory in every primary school. (At the moment English is still compulsory but only in secondary school.) I can understand words written down because we were always reading but speaking is difficult. When I am speaking I must think for a long time for words and I worry that people will get bored. My friend Grace in the Oxfam shop told me 'don't worry, don't worry, slowly, you can speak slowly.' But I still worry. She gives me advice and tells me 'gradually it will come and you will speak.'

I remembered that when I was working in the charity shop in my country, the Bam earthquake happened. It was close to where I lived. Everybody helped the people who were hurt or lost everything. The

British and Americans sent lots of boxes. The people didn't know the name on the boxes. 'Oxfam,' they said, 'what does it mean?' They thought it was the government but really it was the people from Oxfam.

Now I know that Oxfam is a huge organisation, very busy and helpful for all the world. I am happy to work for it and I am going to stay there forever. I love Oxfam and I love to work with the people there.

Interview by Jeni Williams

Rhian Saadat

Desperately Seeking Ziryab

It was in the square at Serpa that we decided to keep going East, even if it had us driving in circles, and in spite of the freezing fog. Pedro had drawn us a map – a straight road, with his only English word – NO – written either side. Hadi said it used to be like that in Iran; it was considered impolite to suggest that the weary traveller's route could be anything other than in whatever direction he already faced. People had always crossed each other's kingdoms, had always taken the short cut along the garden path. Accepting this, we decided that Pedro the petrol pump attendant had indeed sported a Middle Eastern look, and could well have inherited genes from a world before that had refrained from saying things like You have made a mistake. We were, in fact, on a family quest to help our older son find the crossroads of Persian and flamenco music. Half Iranian, half Welsh, through the learning of palos and compas-bulerias, malaguenas, soleas, alegrias – he had become entranced – fascinated by the rhythms and the patterns of this music that wasn't his, and yet, he had explained, he felt he'd known all his life. Over the last thousand kilometers or so, a tired silence had grown between us that was strangely full of promise. We were expectant. But we were running out of time, and more often than not, lost.

A guitar maker in Seville – Jose Postigo – whilst reforming one of his ateliers in the Santa Cruz quarter of the city had stumbled upon an early instrument quickly identified as one of those owned by the great and ancient Ziryab. Postigo wished to present it to the city. Arab musicologists claimed this influential performer as an Arab, the Persians acknowledged him as Persian, and the Syrians were insisting he belonged to them. The Spanish as yet were undecided, not wanting to fully recognize the weight of his work. They were happy to bestow him on Cordoba for the interim. Revisionists are slow in their revisions. But the fact remains that eight hundred years ago, Ziryab was an immigrant genius, living in Spain. The story had appealed to my son and he simply wanted to attend the ceremony, take photographs, and we had said alright.

But we needed to stop. From the pitted main road, this frontier town promised little, and yet gave us much in the way of urgent comfort. The curd cakes were cheap and the best we'd ever tasted, and Anoush earned us a little money at the gates of the castle, playing fandagos, and his own version of Domeniconi's Anatolian Suite. I made a quick scribble in my notes: Still travelling, and photographed Hadi and Shahram outside the ancient apothecary. More South America than Europe, I added as an afterthought. The shop was shiny and ancient, the people brown. I bought wool from a shop that could have been imported from my grandmother's village in South Wales; I had no plans to knit – I needed to keep an eye on the map – and simply wanted to buy the memory of a cave-dark interior, the smell of neat brown yarn still in its cellophane, on a top shelf in a shop that was also brown, and silent, and constantly arranged – and the only things moving were motes of dust and a secret, distant cat.

By the time we reached the province of Huelva, the mist was beginning to dilute itself in the thin, liquid sun, leaving us as witnesses – the only ones on earth, it seemed – to an endless march-past of ancient oaks, and buckled pastures, and scruffy-wig stork nests punctuating the route. It was April, and still raining in the Sierra Morena; we would leave the mountains quickly – cross the ford at Alajar – and then hit the Guadalquivir sometime around lunch. That would leave us about half an hour to park behind the Maria Luisa gardens and make our way to the shop. Tight, but possible.

It's hard to chart the origins of an obsession; my son's began probably before he was born. Hadi, my husband, and I moved to Paris on a whim, one New Year's Day. Whilst he went to the Sorbonne to conjugate verbs, I stayed home listening to his extensive collection of Persian music. In our respective ways, we were trying to graft onto ourselves a little of another culture. It was to be our common ground. Our first son, Anoush, was born loving the sound of the se-tar, the oud and the kamancheh, but it was a guitar I bought him eventually – a quarter-size – from a small Spanish-owned 'taller' just off the rue Rome. To begin with, it was the little mulberry wood and long-fretted lute-like se-tar that he wanted to play. Hadi had bought it during a recent visit to Tehran. It was light and ancient, with a small, closed face. It reminded me of a visitor who had yet to learn our language – or we his. For a child, it was a delight – adjustable frets and ideal for small, delicate hands, but the only teacher we could find was a political refugee who lived on the seventh floor of a sloping building. He played music that was full of sadness, and left us all depressed and full of abstract longings that made us uncomfortable and wrong. Hastily, we put the visitor aside, making a mental note to keep looking for a teacher, and the little guitar was finally brought out, dusted and tuned. Of course, Anoush has moved on since

91

then; grown too, and now owns a couple of full-size, spruce and cedar Sanchez brutes (and the little guitar has been passed down to our second son). Anoush's guitar teacher – Señor Andres Serrita of Barcelona and Saint-Denis – unearthed the young boy's latent love of Aeolian modes and Persian notes. That was when he started to take an interest in the roots of this music, tracing it all the way into himself.

The traffic was knotted and angry along the banks of the river. Pedro's map had been useful on the open road, but made no sense in the tangle of horse-drawn carriages and throbbing hatchback cars. We darted into a side street just after the canary yellow bullring, and ran, leaving the guitar stowed safely in the boot. The Ziryab Ceremony was to take place beneath the Giralda Tower, and we would make it. Just.

And then, a fork in the road, and we chose the left street, when we should have taken the right. Half way down, in a three-storey merchant house, a door opened suddenly, and we caught the magical strains of flamenco guitars and a cajon drum and some other gorgeous sound immediately familiar to all of us. And, unable to move away, we noticed that someone was playing a small mulberry se-tar so that it throbbed energetically beneath the rasciados of the guitars. It offered a new voice to the traditional; something flung further back in the history of sound, and yet, not a visitor at all, but there because it belonged. Anoush was rooted to the spot, finally entering further into the courtyard. We were received with nods and signals to stay, and the Ziryab Ceremony was forgotten – because we'd found him living in this cross-cultural exchange, when we had presumed him long dead.

Anoush heard later that Postigo had presented the mayor with a small and simple fretted instrument rather like a lute, and that it had been whisked away very quickly, to be embalmed in an archive of cloth and glass. No one would ever play it of course. It would serve as a piece of evidence; not as proof that Ziryab had existed – they'd need more than a simple instrument – but that his essence had.

It was time to head home. Staring at the rush hour traffic heading out of the city, we wondered whether we should retrace our route, if only to ask Pedro to draw us a new map. And then decided that, on this occasion, we wouldn't. Serpa would have to wait until another day. We wanted to get back to Paris, if only to find another teacher, and to tune up the little Persian lute.

Trezza Azzopardi

Maria, in the World

On the doormat, he finds two pieces of junk mail, a card from the Post Office, and a plain blue envelope with her writing on the front. He tears it open as he makes his way to the kitchen, dragging his finger along the edge and pulling out the single sheet of Basildon Bond. He knows before he unfolds the paper what it will say: this would be the tenth such note he's received. He isn't surprised, then, when he reads:

Cardiff bus station, Tuesday 11th , 5pm.

She never signs the notes, and the stationery is always different, but always vaguely similar; something you'd find on a low shelf in the shop-cum-post office, next to the cardboard box of elastic bands and the canisters of Raid, all covered in a film of dust. She would have bought a biro from the same shop, and although the ink was sometimes black and sometimes blue, the words she wrote, the instructions, as he thinks of them, never altered: place, day, date, and time. Nothing else, nothing else to go on, the bare skeleton of a message.

The very last time he saw Maria in the flesh, they were in the car. They'd just taken their dog out for a walk in the woods, and he was listening to the football commentary on the radio. She had been talking for five minutes, about Matt and Cara, who were coming for dinner that evening. She didn't care for Cara, who looked like a sheep, Maria said, and made about as much sense. She was still going on; he could hear the name Cara, then a drone of detail, then Rob, which was his own name, Rob, you aren't listening, are you? And then, more emphatic, Robert!

So he tuned back in to Maria, his eyes on the road and a hot feeling on his chest, as if he'd got sunburnt there: someone – he couldn't catch who – had just scored a goal. Without thinking, he leaned over and turned the volume up; the combined noise of the crowd and the commentator drowned Maria out.

He remembers it as if it were yesterday, every detail, and recognizes, too, that some of his recollection would be fact, and some invention. He has lived through the moment so often that the memory has acquired, like a stone in water, a smooth, round shape in his mind.

They are approaching the traffic lights on the junction of Newport Road. Maria has stopped mid-sentence and is groping in the ashtray for loose change, clawing the coins into her palm. She is wearing a pair of ripped jeans, his old blue fleece, her walking boots. Her hair, tied back in a knot, is slightly greasy. She's wearing no make-up. Rob pulls up behind the car in front, and as he slows to a stop, she flings open the passenger door. And then she's gone. He has time to take a surprised, sideways glance at her as she moves behind the car, walking in a straight line out of the sunshine and into the deep shade of a tall building, where she is lost among the shoppers. There are cars behind him, and cars in front, a no right turn sign, people crossing at the corner of the street, and Rob remembers it all in present tense, as if it's still happening, as if he could stop himself leaning over and turning up the radio, as if he could put a hand on the back of her neck – the bit where her hair had come away from the band in sweaty ringlets – and stroke it. As if the act of tuning her out had made her disappear.

He ponders this again, leaning against the fridge, feeling its low hum in the small of his back. He puts the folded note to his nose.

His immediate reaction wasn't so tender. He remembers thinking that she was a bloody stupid woman, and where did she think she was going? It was not a thought which had any edge to it then, although over the years it would acquire its own particular sharpness, stabbing him repeatedly in the sternum. Where did she think she was going?

He carried on as normal that day; fed the dog, went to the supermarket and bought food for that evening's dinner party, aware that the longer she stayed out, the more his insides bloomed with rage. As the evening approached, he took the dog for a turn in the park, and thought about cancelling Cara and Matt.

Cara didn't seem too worried about Maria, although she agreed, it would be wise to cancel. And Rob spent that night at home alone, not realizing it would be the first of many.

At two in the morning, while he was drunk, he phoned the hospitals, then the police, who sent a police officer round the next day with a notebook. She took a description and asked him questions. Had he contacted relatives and friends? Had she been acting strangely at all? Did he know of anything troubling his wife? History of depression? Did she have any money on her? Did they have a joint bank account? Had they argued? No, no, and no. But he did know her pin number, he said, so he would check her account. At this, the constable fixed a steady gaze on him but said nothing. She went away, adding that if he were to hear from his wife, he should contact the station. She managed to make it sound as if that would be exactly what would happen.

Maria's bank account remained untouched. None of her friends knew where she might be, or, Rob supposed, if they did, they weren't telling him. He took the dog out in the mornings and got drunk in the evenings. After a week, he went back to the police. They agreed that his wife was now officially a missing person, and took him into a room where they asked him more probing questions, about what he did for a living, what she did, how they met, what they liked to do, why they had no children, whether they had affairs. All sorts of personal questions which were prefaced with, I know this seems a funny thing to ask, or, We'd like you to cast your mind back... and Rob really tried, squeezing his eyes tight as if the answers would appear on the insides of his eyelids. The questions grew more insinuating. What had he done immediately after she'd got out of the car? Had he tried to follow her? Had he considered that she might be unwell? Had he phoned around when he got home? He'd waited? He'd walked the dog? He'd gone shopping?

So it was a relief when one bright morning the following week, the same policewoman turned up on the doorstep.

We have some news, she said, nearly smiling, as if to assure Rob that it wasn't bad news he was about to hear. They had located CCTV footage of someone who could be his wife; would he care to come to the station to view it?

He was amazed to see how clear the first pictures were; could read not only his car number plate but the faded Dragon sticker in the back window. He caught sight of Dennis, their dog, leaping up from the back seat. He forgot to concentrate on the flash of Maria's form as she slammed the door of the car and moved away: the officer had to wind it back and show him again. He couldn't remember her slamming the door – but then the football commentary was on, he'd turned volume right up. The second piece of video, from a camera trained on the wall of the high building, was less distinct. It showed her, grainy and foreshortened, moving quickly through the mass of people. She looked out of place without a handbag or shopping, her arms swinging at her sides. He agreed that it was indeed Maria, but he couldn't read her face.

Rob puts the note on top of the fridge and considers the magnets stuck to the door: a plastic souvenir of Castell Coch, a picture of Dennis as a pup, a ceramic ice cream cone, and a large metal disc that spun out of a Christmas cracker and which now hides a rusted chip in the enamel. He removes them, throwing them all in the bin-liner in the centre of the kitchen floor. After a minute, he pauses, retrieves the photo of Dennis and places it face down on top of the note from Maria.

Those following months, Rob gave interviews to the police, to a detective, to a newspaper, and got a slot on local radio to make an appeal. There were sightings of Maria as far away as Glasgow, and one promising but fruitless tip-off that she was living in a squat down the docks. He put up poster-sized pictures of her in any public venue which would let him; pubs and supermarkets and corner shops, until they faded, got replaced, or, in one case, until he couldn't bear to look at her face any more every time he passed the post office, and asked them to take it down. He was offered counselling, which he refused, and drifted away from most of his friends. He drank steadily, not to blur the pain, but to entice it towards him. After nine months, he still listened for a key in the door.

Thirteen months after her disappearance, on a bitter March morning, the first of the notes arrived. It was so unexpected, Rob didn't realize at first that it was Maria's sloping script on the envelope. The message inside read:

The Lion, Friday 7th, 5pm.

The bar was crowded with groups of perfumed young women and slicked-back men in suits; office workers getting an early start on the weekend. Rob felt strange to be in company again, under-dressed and over-aged. After checking the bar, he ordered a pint of Guinness and sat on a bench just behind the door. He imagined watching Maria as she came in. She'd look around the pub, she wouldn't see him immediately. He realized that he was picturing her, not as he last saw her, but as he first saw her, when her hair was longer and she was thinner, a little too thin in those days, and smartly dressed. She was going for an interview with a sales company, and had gone alone into the Lion to get a 'steadier' for her nerves. They chatted, and she smiled a lot, showing the gap between her two front teeth. She had a habit of tracing her forefinger across her forehead, as is testing an invisible scar. An hour later, and she'd decided she didn't want the job, anyway, which she said sounded a bit dry. He asked her out to dinner.

Three pints in, the bar crammed with different people who looked even younger than the original crowd, and Rob realized Maria wasn't going to turn up. Afterwards, he spent months thinking it through. Perhaps she had come in when he'd gone to the toilet? Or maybe she'd seen him, reflected in the mirrors above the bar, sitting there in his old denim shirt, slugging his beer, his eyes wandering to the match on the big screen, and she'd thought against it. He remembered the teams, the score, who scored, when. He remembered making room on the bench for a couple of girls who looked so beautiful, radiantly young, and who laughed like witches. He went back to the bar, just the once, to relive the evening he'd waited, telling himself it was not in the hope of meeting those girls again, but to time himself going to the toilet. He had three pints; the girls didn't show.

He puts a piece of stale bread in the toaster and throws the wrapper in the bin-bag on top of the fridge magnets and old tins of food and unwanted crockery. The bag is nearly full, and quite heavy, so he ties the plastic straps into bunny ears and unfurls another. He flicks it open with a violent flourish.

There were other times when Maria didn't turn up: he remembers them all. A spring day in 1998, two years almost to the day since she'd gone, when he was instructed to go to Cardiff Castle and wait at the Animal Wall. Standing beneath a crouching leopard, Rob got it into his head that he was being watched. It made him anxious, made his skin itch. He convinced himself that she was watching him, from a café opposite. He abandoned his post after only an hour, went and sat in a window seat in the café, just where he thought she would have been watching. He told himself that it was better to see her first, when she came, than to hang about under a stone beast, looking like a pervert. He'd shown the police that letter. They seemed unusually preoccupied by the fact that he hadn't told them about the first one. They asked him more questions, about life insurance, whether she'd made a will. Finally, they asked for a sample of her handwriting. It all made him feel like he had something to hide. When they were convinced that it really was Maria sending the notes, they lost interest.

It proves she's still in the world, a different policewoman said, So there's hope, isn't there?

Millennium Eve, he was instructed to go to a bridge near Tongwynlais. He waited, with the water rushing wildly below him and his throat as dry as road dirt. He'd forgotten that Maria had brought him to this place before. They'd made love in the woodland below Castell Coch, and afterwards joked about fairytale princesses and scary trolls. Rob stood alone on the bridge while a thousand fireworks cracked open the sky above him; below, at the water's edge, he caught a flash of movement. It

97

looked like someone kneeling. After staring for a while, he realized it was a sodden piece of cardboard caught in an overhanging branch.

After his compassionate leave ended, Rob went back to editing his software manuals. He found that if he promised himself a morning on the streets, he could get an afternoon's work done. He didn't do anything particular in the city, just wandered around, thinking he might see her face. He always started where he last saw her, but often he ended up miles out of town, reaching into the suburbs or the start of the countryside. Sometimes he took Dennis, trying not to think of him as a lure. Then the Internet took off and he found he could search online. When Dennis died, Rob gave up the walking entirely, and got not so much fat as waterlogged, as if his muscles had turned into filled balloons.

She would never have gone without taking Dennis. This is what he told the police, when they were trying to explain to him that some people do just vanish. They go without warning, they said, without thinking. The longer they're gone, the harder it is for them to come back. One raw-faced young constable suggested the missing person's help-line, as if Rob hadn't already given them her details. They have experienced bereavement counsellors, the young officer said, as if this news would cheer him up. Rob decided that if he uttered the word bereavement again, he'd be forced to hit him. And he'd reply, to whoever listened, Maria might not have wanted to stay with me, but she would never have gone without Dennis.

Rob tells himself this again. Even though he's leaving their house for a memory-free apartment down the Bay, he'll take the picture of Dennis. When she does come back, she'll at least have that. He's packed the butter away, so he eats the toast dry and cold, then unplugs the toaster and the fridge, pulling the door open wide. The room grows immediately darker, as if he had switched off the lights. He sees rain on the window, and his own face staring back. He has thought of Maria, of little else, since her vanishing. He imagines her captor, making her write the notes, all ten of them – or more, maybe, maybe there's more to come – in a single sitting. He imagines him, it would be a him, choosing the times and locations as if he inhabited Rob's history, their history, as if he has stalked them for years. Rob has imagined her kidnapped and murdered, has seen her fingernails broken and bloody from the struggle, has seen her drugged and raped, locked and starving in a cellar, suffocated, stabbed, doused with petrol, and dumped in a landfill site. Or, he thinks of her alone and mystified in a B&B in Penarth, struggling with who she is, drinking gin from the bottle. Lying in the basement of a block of flats with a slick of grime on her cheek. Sitting in the rain on a bench in an un-named town, staring at the tarmac. Once a year, in a lucid moment, she puts pen to paper and calls him back. And then she forgets what she's done, where to go, when.

All horrors come in with the darkness. He welcomes them because the alternative is unthinkable: he can't bear to imagine her walking out in the sunshine with a new woollen fleece and her hair shining, her wide, gap-toothed smile, a black and white dog turning a frenzy of loops at her feet. He couldn't bear to suffer for that kind of possibility.

The rain falls heavily, splotching the cardboard box he's carrying, depositing trembling droplets on the chrome surface of the toaster. He opens the boot and heaves the box in on top of the others. He will not have a last check round. As he drags the bin-bags along the side passage and lines them up in a neat row with the others, Rob looks back down the street. He considers leaving a forwarding address. He considers life with a view of the water, a new relationship, a new beginning; so many considerations that he arrives at the inevitable: finally, he considers a woman in an old fleece, sitting in a Perspex bus shelter, waiting. He pulls at the brass handle of the letter-box, and sees again the letters, plain blue Basildon Bond, dropping silently onto the carpet, year in, year in, year out.

Zoulikha Zaidi

Oppression

Those who are lucky enough to live in safer places and more democratic societies don't realise how important it is to feel free to express yourself without the fear of imprisonment or killing, to dress the way you want and not face harassment or assault, to feel safe when walking in the street without the fear of being attacked or killed. Those people just take these valuable and priceless things for granted.

Depending on personalities when facing oppression, some people give up and let others rule their lives, while others become more rebellious and fight till they get their rights. At the end of their fight, they may feel weaker, but in reality they are stronger.

Fleeing one's home country is never an easy task. In some societies, when a woman leaves her country, it is already a breach of the 'Holy' social rules, and she rarely gets support from her own family; regardless how vital it is for her to leave. The rule is, you have committed the crime of being a woman so you should accept, obey, be a minor forever and never argue with any social or religious rules.

For women who are lucky and strong enough to leave oppressive countries, being in Britain is not the end of the journey. Seeking asylum is a long and painful struggle, dehumanizing and depressing. In addition to the pressure of the asylum process itself, there may be problems with language and childcare, and encountering a new culture where they are expected to take charge and make decisions means that they have to continue to be both strong and lucky. Failing to be so with the Home Office will probably lead to disaster.

Most women's asylum cases are not dealt with fairly by the Home Office because it fails to adhere to its own Gender Guidelines, because of negative stereotyping from solicitors, interpreters, caseworkers and/or support workers, or simply because many of the women seeking asylum are not used to taking responsibilities or initiatives.

Being granted Leave to Remain in Britain is not the end of the tunnel. Now you don't have to hide because you are an asylum seeker, but you have to hide because you are not employed. Being a refugee living off the British taxpayer is not something you can be proud of. We come to Britain for safety and freedom but we need dignity, too. This dignity can only be acquired if we can support ourselves and not feel or appear as parasites.

Section 4

STRUGGLE

. . . this home is not for me . . .

Afsaneh Firoozyar

Some Day

I went to the balcony
I looked at the sky
Oh, the sky and stars were very beautiful
But my feelings were very bad
I could not enjoy the sky and stars

Some day we need a new revolution

I went to the beach.
Oh, the beach was very beautiful.
But this beach was not for me.
Here all the people were friendly
But I was not happy

Some day we need a new revolution

No-one has invited me to the sun
No-one has taken me to the sparrows' feast
Here all the angels are crying for me
But I have lost my heart

This home is not for me
I am thinking of a different home, with lots of lights.
Oh, that home is very beautiful
But it is not for me

My mother is sitting under the lights
She is waiting, waiting for me

Some day we need a new revolution

Carolyn Edge

After the News

Tonight my bed is warm
No icy ground damp under me
No cursing strangers either side
No shivering child blue-lipped under my arm

Tonight my bed is soft
No coarse blankets over rocky earth
No choking dust or seeping wet
No kicks from hostile boots deny me rest

Tonight my bed is safe
No piercing fear of dark to come
No crushing loss, no hollow grief
No fires to wrench me gasping from my sleep

Tomorrow holds more hope than hell
More love than hate, more life than death
But oh my brothers...
I thank my God I am not there
And pray He holds them tightly in His palm

Elizabeth Baines

Star Things

'There's things like stars in the stream.'
Angela Johnson nudges the gate.
'Come on,' says Angela Johnson, lolling her eyes about. Angela Johnson has socks that disappear down her sandals. She jumps on the gate and makes it swing inwards.
You should go straight home.
'Come and see the star things.'
My Daddy's got a star thing, a thing called a meteorite, out of the sky.

At Angela Johnson's, when you call in the morning, there's a man sitting in the shadows who Angela Johnson ought in all decency not to call Daddy. Sunshine lops across the breathless dust of the sideboard and over the table, making bacon rinds oozy. The shadows around seem to wriggle. Angela Johnson's mother, still in her dressing gown, hardly says anything, and nothing at all about going straight home.
Angela Johnson's mother gets children while she's blinking.
Angela Johnson gets her clothes handed down. As she leans on the gate her dress that used to be her sister's goes up at the back and down at the front to her ankles.
'No one will know.'
The wood is black and yellow bars dipping over the hill crest.
No one knows where the Johnson children come from. No one knows where they go. Everyone knows what the business was their father went away on; some can guess why he broke down the back door with a hatchet.
In the wood there's something cracking.
Angela Johnson leaves the gate swinging. Down the hill there are boys, Johnson boys and others, breaking branches and slinging them. They jump, knees bent, swinging, till the whole tree winces; twigs and leaves spark and sizzle as they hurl them down the slope.
'Don't worry, no one will see.'
My Daddy might come looking.
For children like the Johnsons the Social Services come looking. Children like the Johnsons have heads that are alive.
The boys come round, fists like pebbles in their pockets, legs in corrugated socks, their cropped hair bristling in the sun.

'Your dad's a Jew, then, isn't he?'

My Daddy's got a star that fell out of the sky.

'What star? Hah!' Doubled up, snorting, kicking the tree trunks, throwing sticks looping upwards. 'Got a star, my eye!'

Yes, he has, he's got a meteorite he found while he was walking.

'You're joking, what's it look like?'

Split across, and in the middle there's a wheel shape all in silver.

Elbows leaning on the tree now. 'What's it made of?'

The meteorite lies in the glass-fronted cabinet. No one knows where it came from, no one knows what it's made of. Perhaps you better hadn't touch it.

Don't go too close to children whose bodies might be crawling. Don't let them get too near. Just in case, let's do your hair with a fine-toothed dust comb; scrub your nails and keep them short or you might catch worms.

'Your mam wears a hat, I seen her, and goes to church on Sundays.'

The Johnson children's mother wear a coat with half its buttons, no wonder when she's passing she turns her head as though she's wincing: you wonder really how she dares to walk abroad at all.

My Daddy's got a star that fell while he was winking.

'What's the colour of the star, then?'

Once it was red-melting, but now it's black and silver.

'Ha!' Dancing off, sending currents of stone-flight out through the bracken: 'Her dad got bird shit in his eye!' Flicking back: 'What's it feel like?'

You're not supposed to know, remember, better hadn't touch it. Once it was on fire, but it must have been cooling when he put it in his pocket.

'So where did he find it?'

No one knows. No one knows how far he'd been when he walked abroad. And by the time he brought it home it had gone stone cold.

And weren't there lots of questions? And didn't someone call out in the night time? And then they made the rule about the glass-fronted case.

Now the boys are off, lolloping, spinning sticks at blackbirds to make them go cack-crackling, looking for a spot that's flat enough for marbles.

Angela Johnson's tugging: 'Let's go to the stream.'

The sun's getting lower, the air fizzing with midges, flicking on and off in pinpoints. Baubles of stained sunshine smash across the ground.

One of the Johnsons has a scar across his forehead.

Johnson children get dropped from their prams.

'What's the meteor's shape?'

Like a chopped-off finger, a knobbly knuckle.

The Johnson boy's scar jumps like forked lightning: 'Ha! Someone threw her dad a knuckle bone!'

My Mummy's got a scar that she covers up with powder. Powdered skin is sweet and dry, has a perfume that lingers after someone's gone to church. Be careful near the dressing table, all those bowls and cut-glass bottles: scent that's been spilled stains the polished surface, and powder makes a breathless cloud...

Angela Johnson slithers off down the tussocks. Golden kingcups in the water, oily with the sunshine.

Stars that ooze and bubble from the mud that you could slip on.

You can slip on the mud and badly scar your cheekbone, lose your hat and scar your cheekbone; run through mud with a pushchair, banging, slipping on the grass slope, suddenly tumbling backwards, wheels upended, spinning. You'll be lying cheek down, sobbing: there's no getting away, you can't undo the mistake you made.

Now the boys come swaggering, lice in their heads and wriggling worms inside their bellies, throwing pebbles, knocking kingcups, punching holes in the water.

Don't throw stones.

Don't throw anything.

Don't throw powder bowls and bottles...

'Hey, here's your dad, here's the Jew!'

Run, and the sun's clip-clipping the branches; nearer: light slicing the grasses; grasp his knuckles: it's so late, the way home now has different shadows.

My Daddy's got a star that hit the earth and died.

Farzaneh Dadkhah

Maybe Maybe

Maybe it is too much
    lots of burden on our shoulders
Maybe it is too much
    all this sadness for us
Maybe it is too much
    all this responsibility for us
Maybe it is too much
    all these bitter memories

Maybe
Maybe

Maybe it is not too much for freedom
For all these sufferings for our hometown
Maybe it is not too much
For the laughter of children in the mother's embrace

Maybe it is not too much to have food
For all the hungry people

To work for freedom in our country

In Iran

I want to tell you lots of things about the regime in Iran.

When I am young, the Mujahadin made demonstration and made meetings for two and a half years. But when the regime arrived and we tried to have meetings there were always people from the government who tried to beat people up. They came to the meetings with chomagh [sticks] which they would use to beat people. One time my husband came away from a meeting and he was cut with a knife on this leg. He was so busy trying to run away he had not even noticed he was bleeding. Someone with a knife just cut at his leg.

We are all Muslims in Iran but we have different beliefs. The government is pretending to be Muslim. They have brought different things that are not in our holy book and put it in the law. The people in the parliament in Iran are not like most of the people in Iran. But they just say, 'This way is the Islamic way.'

Then after that the regime came into the street with guns and catch the Mujahadin group. The regime caught half a million people. 120 people were killed in public and they didn't even have any evidence about what they said they have done. They didn't give them a proper trial. My brother was in the court for just two minutes. He was seventeen years old. In the court the judge just lined up twenty people and he went down the line and said to one person, 'You will be killed,' and to the next person, 'You will be in prison for life.' When they got to the last person, that person was laughing so the judge went back and said he would be killed.

It is difficult as a woman in Iran. There is no equality between men and women. Always men are first and have more rights. Women are just for sex and to bring babies. But women are very active in Iran. Islam never tells you that women are different than men. When our prophet went to Mecca, in that time people used to have slaves and he told them that they are not different from the slave and there is no difference between women and men, you are all just people, you have to treat them equally.

I had a lot of things happen in my life. My mother-in-law's sister was 62 years old. They catch her for six years. The regime tortured me, they raped my sister. I got depressed but my sister she is very strong. The regime caught my husband three times. There were times when my husband was in the prison and I was in the prison as well and my twin daughters were five months old. I had to bring my daughters up myself. When one daughter was nineteen she was in another city in Iran and then she became ill and the hospital wasn't good. She died. She was only twenty.

For two years after that we were still in Iran and we were very active. My habit was to go with people, with my group. I was active because I wanted all the government to go, if you know how it feels when someone has died, the person who is left wants revenge for what has happened. And you don't change the regime unless all of them go.

Me and my second daughter were very active. When my daughter was in the university she was politically active. They tried to find my daughter. My daughter was lucky because she was not home but they found my husband instead. When you are in Iran and they can't catch you they catch the family. They ask him questions. We had to run away. We came out of the country. I wanted to come here and have freedom and be active.

When I am coming here I have problem because the Iranian people can't go back to Iran. The Home Office knows this. But they don't let the children go into the education, go to university. This is bad because it means that they are not useful for the society.

I want a secular regime in Iran because in Iran there are different religions living. I want everyone to be able to tell everything, to say everything. We want power for the people, not power for groups.

Farzaneh Dadkhah was interviewed by Heaven Crawley

Fridah Kimani

Through the Eyes of a Window

Take me, I'm a window.
I have lots of different feelings,
especially Lonely and Hated.

Lonely because no one looks or cleans me,
they just walk past and take no notice.

Hated because of my owners.
They have people chucking eggs and stones
and I take the hate not them.

What if I fall to pieces, my soul will be broken
and someone else will take my place

I know I'm hated and I feel lonely
but PLEASE don't BREAK my SOUL

OH NO! I can see a stone coming my way,
what shall I do?

This might be my last moment...

Hamira Ageedy

The Fifty-Nine Innocent

When they fought again their father was angry and upset. 'What's the matter? What's this squabble about?' he asked.

'Nothing,' said Mother. 'Leave them alone. I asked Aria to speak to him.'

Mr Ahmad became angrier and interrupted his wife, 'Speak about what? Why am I the last person to be informed about every problem?'

Mrs Maryam tried again: 'Please don't shout. I asked Aria to speak to him about the danger of this war. He's determined to enrol in the army.' One year after the revolution when Ayatollah Khomeini came to power, the Iraqi army had attacked Iran.

'I don't understand why children never listen or understand their parents,' said Mr Ahmad apprehensively.

Eighteen years earlier, when his wife had become pregnant after having three girls, his mother had told him, 'I'm sure that this time your wife will give you a son.'

'There is no difference between having a boy or a girl, mum,' said Mr Ahmad.

'There is a big difference, my son,' answered his mother. 'Girls will get married and leave you, but sons stay with their father.'

Mr Ahmad's opinion was different. He had three educated daughters and was very proud of them, but still, he knew that his wife wanted a son. He prayed wholeheartedly for her to have a boy and for her not to be in danger.

'I told you, Ahmad, that God is generous,' Mrs Maryam said excitedly, 'He gave us twins, two sons!' Mr Ahmad was over the moon. After so many years God had given him *two* sons.

It was calamitous that both now wanted to leave their home. Mr Ahmad believed in God and attempted to be patient. 'Oh God, you give them to me and you are supposed to save them. But you know that our country stands on the brink of many crises after this revolution and there is no place for us to be safe.'

When Mother called everyone to breakfast, Aria and Armin entered the room in silence. From their appearance it was clear that things were still contentious. As mother was pouring from the china teapot the front door opened with the recoil of a rifle. Everybody froze.

'Don't move! Hands up!' shouted a pasdar [Iranian Revolutionary

Guard], pointing the rifle towards them. He turned to his colleagues. 'Take away these two saboteurs!' Mother's face paled. She leant against the wall behind. Dry mouth, confused. When she heard the man's voice her eyes widened and she moved towards her sons. The pasdar shouted, 'Stop, or I kill you all!'

Mr Ahmad, bewildered, tried to control himself and spoke humbly: 'Please, tell us what we have done wrong. What is our sin?'

'You shut up! You bastards all try to help your partisans, and pretend you're not.'

Mr Ahmad was determined to do something. Suddenly he rushed over to the Koran on the shelf, and picked it up. 'I swear on this holy book that my sons have done nothing wrong. This is Aria, he's going to study at university in Tehran. And Armin decided to join the army only today,' said Mr Ahmad.

The gunman pushed Armin to the opposite wall with his gun. 'You're a clumsy, fucking lying bastard. You're all lying. I'm taking your bastard sons. Hojatoleslam, Imam Khomeini's commissioner, has come from Tehran and he'll decide whether your motherfucking sons have done anything wrong or not. He knows how to make them to own up.' He shouted at his friends to take them out.

A flush of anger came to Mother's face. She lost control, crying, 'You're going to torture my children for things they did not do! I've heard of what your Hojatoleslam has done in other cities in Kurdistan. He suffocates those voices that cry for freedom. I'm sure Ayatollah Khomeini never ordered the punishment of innocent people.'

The pasdar commander pressed his rifle to Aria's chest and thundered, 'How can you pretend you're innocent? You all want Kurdish autonomy, and we reckon that's a big sin.'

'Do you know what autonomy means?' protested Aria as he was pushed outside by one of the pasdars. 'Asking for some facilities and studying in our language. There are no jobs here, no proper medical services, no universities. Our men have to leave their families all year and look for jobs in other parts of Iran. Do you know how many families have left their lands and are working in the brick-works? We are Iranians too. We are human beings.'

The Commander hit Aria from behind, just as he crossed the threshold of the front door. 'Shut up, you bastard! I'll show you what autonomy means!'

Aria stumbled on the first step and fell down. Mother tried to stop the pasdar hitting her son but it was too late. The gunmen dragged Aria and

Armin outside. They heard the car leave their street.

Mother, crying and tearing at her face, shouted at her husband, 'Why didn't you lock the door? You didn't lock the door again! You didn't lock the door again! You sent my children to the slaughterhouse!'

Mr Ahmad tried to soothe his wife: 'I didn't know there were any problems today. I bought bread from the bakery and came home. Nothing was wrong outside. I just forgot to lock the door. Don't worry my love. Pray for them. Our children are innocent. God will save them.'

'Leave me alone. You're lying. You deliberately didn't lock the door.'

Mr Ahmad's wife was right; he had deliberately left the door open, as most of the people in the city did. There were no more partisans there, but soldiers and pasdars were trawling the city to intimidate people. Banned during the time of the Shah, the Kurdistan Democratic Party of Iran had hoped for some Kurdish autonomy after the 1979 revolution. But things had got worse: the new government banned their newspaper, their organisation and their political activities. All parties except the Islamic party were declared illegal. The KDP changed tack. In order to prevent civil war, the partisans left the cities for the mountains, leaving their pacifist leader, Dr Abdul Rahman Ghasemloo, to negotiate with the central government. But instead of negotiating with the Kurdish representatives, the Islamic Republic of Iran had many of them arrested, and nearly all of them were killed. And although the government knew that there were no partisans in the city, they still suspected everyone. Whenever government forces started to fire aimlessly, those outside on the streets had to find places to hide. That was why people left their front doors unlocked. But Mr Ahmad had no idea why the authorities had entered into their house.

*

'By the time I finish high school I'll be strong like Arnie and I'll study to be a big, famous actor,' Bisetoon said to his brother.

Fardad glared at him. 'You've got seven years to wait. Besides, why don't you mention me? We're twins, we have to be together.'

Bisetoon kept his face under the duvet as he said imperiously, 'That's impossible. You've got to take care of mum and dad. I'm the eldest.'

Farhad angrily pulled back the duvet: 'Ridiculous. You were only born half an hour earlier.'

Their father, Mr Blorian heard the children as he cleaned his teeth. He raised his voice, 'Farhad, Bisetoon, aren't you asleep yet? You've got to be up early tomorrow, haven't you?' There was silence as the children pretended to sleep. But they couldn't. They were all excited thinking about their first day at high school, of being heroes and actors, of their new shoes and school bags.

Mrs Mandana, Mr Blorian's wife, was a clever housewife who spent her time rearing and disciplining her children. Mr Blorian was a respectful teacher who loved and cared for his family very much. His twins were only eleven years old, but he had planned their future careers as medical specialists. 'Which specialism, my love?' asked Mandana as she undressed for bed. 'Heart surgeons. We don't have heart surgeons in Kurdistan,' answered Mr Blorian proudly. But the next day both eleven-year-old brothers were arrested on their way to school and condemned as two saboteurs who had stood in the way of the tanks that were crawling through the city.

'I thought they had something hidden in their schoolbags to throw at the tanks,' said the pasdar to his commander.

'Did you find anything?' asked the commander, indifferently.

'No. There are no freedom fighters here. Hojatoleslam's orders are to collect as many people as we can, just to dominate the people and stop the KDP.'

The commander yawned and stroked his beard. 'How many have you collected?'

'Only 59.'

*

15 March, 2000. My last patient, Mrs Zoligha, entered the examination room in my surgery. She was a widow with no income and had lost both her son and her son-in-law. I had told my receptionist to let her come in whenever she needed to see me.

'Doctor, could you check my blood pressure, please? I'm so excited today. I'm sure you remember that my son Karim was one of the 59 innocents arrested in 1980. The Ayatollah is going to release him.'

'Are you sure? Each year they promise to do it but they don't,' I said.

'No, no, I'm sure this time they're serious,' said Mrs Zoliagha. 'Next week will be New Year and the Ayatollah will order an amnesty and let our sons free.' She looked into my eyes. 'You don't look happy with this good news, doctor?'

I tried to avoid her gaze. 'Oh, no, no, I'm so happy, Mrs Zoliagha, I'm just worried about you, if they aren't released this year again.'

I pretended to be happy. As she tied her chador she said nervously, 'I know, you're worried about me. Every year they promise to release our sons, but up until now they've done nothing.' She left the room.

I thought back to a memory from the days when I was a medical student in Tehran, working in psychiatry.

*

'Here's the file of your new patient, doctor,' a nurse had said. 'He's the most interesting we've admitted today.' I read the file of this 'interesting' patient. He had been diagnosed as delusional; he was said to claim to be Eman Zaman [the Last Holy Imam in Shiite belief].

As I closed the file, I heard a gentle young voice behind me. 'One moment please, doctor.'

I turned and saw a very beautiful girl. She was about twenty, medium height, with black eyes and pale skin. Her hair was covered with a light blue scarf. Her eyebrows and eyes were typical of a Persian girl.

'How can I help you?' I asked.

'Please let him stay here. Do not discharge him for a while. I beg you,' she said humbly. 'What do you mean?' I asked. 'I can't explain more. But as long as he stays here, we're all safe. He's my brother.' I was stunned. Then she seemed to vanish before my eyes.

I opened the door to the patient's room. He was alone, lying on a bed, and got up when he saw me. 'Hello doctor. I've been waiting to see you for ages,' he said politely.

'Hello, Mr Nadery.' He was about forty and his hair was half white. I noticed the similarity between him and his sister in his eyes and eyebrows. He invited me to sit down. His voice was relaxed, showing no sign of physical or psychological disease. 'Could you tell me about yourself, your problem,' I asked him.

He spoke for about an hour: how he had trained in Libya for ten years, about his political activities, how he had fought for the Iranian revolution. He spoke about everything except his disease. He talked about his background so seriously and convincingly that I really could not tell whether what he was saying was real or a delusion.

'Mr Nadery, please tell me about your health problems. Why are you here?' I asked him cautiously.

'I'm here because our governor insists that I have delusions. I was working in the west of Iran, in Mahabad. Maybe you know this city? I was deputy governor there two years ago. One day they arrested 59 people on the streets on grounds of being KDP. They killed them all and mutilated their bodies. When I protested, they accused me of having delusions and forced me to resign. There were two twin brothers, Armin and Aria, who were eighteen, and another pair of twins who were only eleven years old. I'll never forget their lovely faces. Bisetoon and Farhad. I can never forget their voices when they were crying and begging Hojatoleslam, Imam Khomeini's commissioner, 'We've done nothing wrong. We only want to be actors when we're eighteen.'

My patient wanted to speak more and more, but I couldn't bear to hear him. I stood up and left the room.

*

I worked in Mahabad for 17 years. Before each New Year celebration, the families of 59 innocent people waited, hoping for their children to come home. But I knew it was useless. I never dared tell any of them about their children's fate. I told myself, 'Let Mrs Zoliagha and the other mothers have hope and be happy for one week in the year.'

Janet Dubé

from **September 2001**

September 10

The field below the right-hand hedge slopes down
and westward towards the river Talog:
the field above the left-hand hedge slopes up
and eastward towards Llanllwni mountain:

but these laid every year for centuries
maybe, are hardly hedges now, grown out
to trees – ash, blackthorn, hawthorn, hazel, ash
again, meeting overhead where the track

narrows, forming a dome over my head
and an arch opening in front of me,
a natural window, like a metaphor
of the great world and the still narrow way.

September 17

The sound of military jets flying
after dark covers the sound of singing
from the telly. *Pay attention, this is war,*
Say the jets. *We are the war machine.*

Afghanistan is a poor country
whose people are trying to leave or dying
of drought and famine. Is it for them the jets
practise over the hills after dark?

or is it for another country
with the wrong lords and a different God?
I too have a different god and pray
for the lords who order the war machine.

September 19

Out of the Towy valley, the little bus
climbs Alltwalis hill, and at the top
turns left to show, beyond the local farms,
further hills and farms below the cloud.

Today the military sculpture
of a jet banks and levels above the ridge,
soundless at this distance, and disappears
into the clouds above Ceredigion.

You needn't believe in God to pray says
the press this week and maybe the moment's
silence in the bus is a prayer that all
may be spared the final wrath of man.

September 20

This is the time of year I moved to Wales,
when clouds are sometimes lower than the hills,
when hills are sometimes veiled behind the clouds
as if too modest for their loveliness.

This is the time of year I moved to Wales,
when sunny days are long and evenings chill,
when apples plums and blackberries are ripe
and onions and potatoes gathered in.

This is the time of year I moved to Wales,
and this is the year the jets are sounding
loud and long each day, their masters
anticipating a different harvest.

September 25

War, recession, mass depression: happy
the arms-traders and armchair terrorists
who wanted this. Their sweating puppets,
politicians, dance the world promising.

What gives me vivid dreams I've no idea:
my mother and my father still alive,
a wise new baby looking up at me,
the garden or the seaside or old friends;

and a path leading down to the beach where
everyone is waiting for me; and then
the path is lost for ever and I wake
thinking *war, recession, mass depression.*

September 28

Yesterday it rained all day and at dawn
already today the wind is rising.
There's a change in the weather and season
of the human heart in this past month.

It takes a village to raise a child said
the wise ones. *Only connect* said another
and now as we watch each other's death
or life up on the screen, we're connected.

It takes a whole village to raise a child
and this is the global village, like it,
whole, or not. If we can't love each other,
best pray for each other's children.

Jeni Williams

Referral to Medical Foundation

Found poem: a form used by the National Asylum Support Service

(i) Preliminaries

> *Please note:*
>> that in order for the Medical Foundation concession
>> regarding accommodation in London
>> to operate
>> the applicant must show that she or he
>> a) is a survivor of torture
>> b) will need ongoing care or treatment
>> c) needs the specialist services of the Medical Foundation

> *Please note:*
>> that the Medical Foundation
>> does not operate
>> access to family, community or other support
>> which are available by other means

> *Please note:*
>> That the Medical Foundation
>> sees only the first 10 people reporting every day
>> Monday to Friday

> *Note:*
>> Please fax this form to the Medical Foundation
>> Please send a copy of the form to the applicant
>> and to our duty case worker

> *Note:*
>> Registration starts every day
>> at 12
>> noon

Section B: History of Torture

Duration:
six days.

Nature of torture:
raped by soldiers;
several times;
repeated over two days;
shouting;
death threats;
put in cell.

Other experiences of organised violence:
saw her sister tortured (face burned in boiling water).

Current mental and physical health (in applicant's own words please):
finds it difficult to talk about effects;
has experienced nightmares.

Referrer's observations and concerns:

Maggie Harris

from The Auction Rooms

Ascension

Rising like a well-spring
like vomit,
upwards through heart and bone
burning the chest, the back of the throat,
desire.

Glass, oak, mahogany
marble-smooth and grained
under-body scored by the thumb-prints
of centuries
the memory of eau-de-cologne,
damask, brocade.

Other bodies now
in parkas and black leather
sharp-eyed as owls
hands running over veneer,
lifting, stroking, estimating

nostrils, ears, fingers engaging
spirits, pulses, prices rising
the auctioneer's volley ricocheting

that last crazy moment of ascension

before levitating
before dropping
like the hammer
to the silent laughter
of lounging, departed souls.

Ancestor on the Auction Block
(after a poem by Vera Bell)

So you:
around whom I've circumnavigated my entire journey
having to be sailor, archaeologist, map-reader, ventriloquist,
dredging, sifting, navigating, alliterating –

I will not repeat here the journeys of others
will not imagine or re-imagine you,
bestow upon you whatever 'voice' they believe to be yours.

No. We know well the scene:
the pen or market square,
an indoor arena out of the rain,
the prising open of jaws,
the peeling apart of vaginal lips.

Let me instead address that hammer who still speaks today
still rises in men's fists over the price of women
veiled in condescension, satire, jest

whilst even I, whose words journey on without me
have stamped indelibly beneath my skin:
Descendant. Colonies.

Nazand Begikhani

At a Happiness Symposium in Wales

A psychologist said
Graveyards may help you feel happier,
visit a graveyard when you are depressed

There is a thin line between life and death, my friend
and I am a graveyard

I am happy to be alive, my friend
After Halabja and Anfal
I am happy to become the voice
of a land
that contains the mass graves of our brothers

There is a thin line between life and death, my friend
There is a thin line between life and death

Rosemary Jones with **Jeni Williams**

Words to Remember

Like
> *village*
> *fields*
> *tanks*
> *dragged*
> *friend*
> *girl friend*
> *tank*

Like
> *gendarme*
> *many*
> *police station*
> *many*
> *rape*
> *many*
> *rape*

Like
> *barrister*
> *appeal*
> *interpreter*
> *court*

Always matter of fact.

She knew the other words.

> Like *husband.*
> Like *houses.*
> Like *fire.*
> Like *uniform.*
> Like *frightened.*

> Like *too sad.* Like *tears.*
> Like *I'm sorry, I'm sorry.*
> Like *my people, my country.*

Rouhi Downing

Asylum Seeker

It is not easy to be a refugee,
There is a limit to what we can do,
We are doomed to remain, anonymous.
To have expectations, hopes.
We obey passively,
Embarrassed by our children in silence.

I ask myself,
Is this the price I must pay?
Is this the sorrow I gain,
In this civilised world
To sorrow for what and whom?
And this is the law of the civilised man?

What forces us to be passive, anonymous, confused?
Our perplexity, and struggle for survival.
This excites the attention of entrepreneurs and illegal employers.
They demand, and we obey, silently, for poor wages.

Yet we have pride as free men and women:
To say 'No' and leave,
To say 'Yes' and live.

The fabric of our existence is only
Shelter, food on charity, illegal work..
If not, you must be punished:
'Out', 'out', 'go back to where you come from.'
This is what an asylum seeker faces.
This is the reality of our existence.

This is what they deserve –
Only to say, 'Yes… yes' to the illegal employer?

'Behind the scenes' there is no hope,
'Behind the scenes' there is no optimism.
'Behind the scenes' I see no present, no future.

There is a boundary that isolates us from one another
Which is
Me as outsider, you inside.

'Us' and 'Other': these are our boundaries.

Who is to judge this statement?
Who is to lay blame on me, being an outsider?
Who are you to tell me this and that?

To tell me to go 'here' and 'there'?
To call me names, to swear at me?

It is not written on the stone who is who and who says what.
We are shadowy figures about whom little or is nothing known.
But touch us we are flesh and blood.

Stevie Davies

Blood on My Tongue: Abu Ghraib

I pity the bombed child
eyeless and motherless.
I can truly empathise:
how sad, it is a shame.

*

Shame on the men
with black hoods
who rose against democracy:
they don't deserve to live.

*

We live for civilisation.
What is more worthy?
Plant the Jack in the desert:
what's better? a bandage?

*

Bandage my eyes
for the television sears them.
I can see round the frame:
shield me from their blood.

*

Blood on my tongue
in my eyes, in my ears.
I don't feel very well.
It's not a nice taste.

*

Taste my conscience,
it's sweet enough, considering
I'm a blind witness.
Put your hood up. And his.

Section 5

FROM SILENCE TO VOICE

. . . and you say / you will write no more poems . . .

Amani Omer Bakhiet Elawad

و تقول

لن اكتُبَكِ بعد الآن قصيده
و هل يعبّركَ الشوقُ دونَ سطورِ
تعزفُ نبضاً... تسطعُ بوحاً
راية صدقٍ... تصدحُ حينا
لحناً صاغ الوجد معاني فريده

و هل تُنبئكَ حروفي انكَ روحي
قلبي و ذاتي.. تهبُّ ثباتي
سُحباً تُمطرُ عشقاً دافئ
فيض فاق حدودَ الوصفِ.. و الكلماتِ
حُلماً اهدي العمر ليالي سعيده

و يكفي أنك بين ضلوعي
مدٌّ يعبّر عُمقَ حدودي
رمزٌ حددَ شكلَ وجودي
فجرٌ حطمَ طوقَ يُودي
ليبقى حُبَك فوقَ الكلمةِ اقوى مني
و تَبقى لكل صباح طلةَ عِيدهَ

And You Say

you will write no more poems.
How can my tenderness utter itself without verses
that set your heartbeats to a music shimmering with ardour?
Truth reveals itself in melodies
whose harmonies frame passion in pure intensity

Do my letters prove that you are my soul, my heart, my being?
that in your presence I discover myself?
The clouds rain warm love,
the flood spills over my words and writings:
your love gifts my life with the happiness of dream.

It is enough that you lie at the core of my soul:
a tide breaching my deepest boundaries,
a star drawing my shape to fuller existence.
Your love is greater than these words, stronger than me:
you are the dawn of my every Eid morning

Translated by Amani Elawad and Jeni Williams

Carol Rumens

Women, Veiled

Because the mouth has been known to tell lies
Because beauty isn't better than compassion
Because we live with two terrors: being looked at, not being looked at
Because we shine without photosynthesis

Because our eyes are lost birds, beating from dark to dark
Because our foreheads were scorched by the explosion
Because you need room for your house, when you must leave it
And because we mourn for the children, butchered in Crazy Park

And because you should give death time, though your body blooms with
plenty
Because you are mostly liquid. Because you need somewhere to laugh
Because you're the sleeve of Allah. Because of the man you have chosen
Because he is simple. Because you have chosen yourself

The Veiled Woman's Ghazal

Do you understand this strange country where clocks 'go back'
And so many small eyes seem to be saying 'Go back'?

Are they scared of a shadow, veiled, on a bland bright dial?
Such ancient clocks are not designed to 'go back.'

Somewhere our summer is smoke, the ground cracks into fire,
No bird is left to scream to the children 'Go back!'

The new recruits skin up and dance at the Victory Disco.
But the eyes that count the dead are saying go back.

Washed in the soaps of this watery, wintery land,
The child groans at the grandparent: 'Don't. Go. Back!'

Can the breast of a story stop the tip of the sword?
The story perches on silence, and silence sighs, go back.

For our sweetest myth is the summer that never changes,
And our bodies are made of stars, for ever begging, go back.

Don't stare at the stars, Shahid, don't swallow the small-eyed winter.
Next year the clocks will go forward. One day we will go back.

Fiona Owen

Magda's Song

No rest, we walk on in silence.
But for the weeping
and the whimpers of the children,
there are no words and my name is lost.

My husband of fifty-two years –
an old man, his veins hardening
and his back weakened from a life of work –
they took, tore from me though I fell to my knees
and beggingly clutched at the legs of men
who held our lives at gunpoint.
What use is he, an old man like him?
No threat to your regime!
But my words were kicked to the door
and out into the mud. See, I have the bruises
though they are numb.

Some of the men they left undead – few –
whose hands still fluttered like shot birds
who think they may yet fly. The rest
they made cattle of, carted off
and oh, that ripped last look he gave me,
my husband of fifty-two years.

Soon we will reach the border
and though I pray with each step I take
for these young ones, these babes,
these widow girls and broken mothers,
for myself, I have nothing to ask.
My feet stumble forwards following
my townsfolk to some sanctuary (they say)
getting away with life still somehow breathing us.
But my soul is not in this nameless shell –
it has spilled out. It is back with the whining dogs,
and the flies already feeding off the dead wounds
of my husband, of fifty-two years.

Forough Farrokhzad

Return

Again, that wall with the old vine:
    I leant against that wall.

There, clear sap was rising like a spring.
    I whispered, Iis that you, Kami?

Through branches rich with leaf,
    I saw the bitter past,

old growth reviving and dusty time.
    Nothing left but a name.

I gazed, longing –
    the road came finally to an end –

Seeking just a trace of him
    I reached the way of dust,

saw only my small room,
    a spring of struggle and regret by my thirsty path.

Empty of his childish cry,
    my city is my tomb.

Translated by Romisa Asadi (with Jeni Williams)

Note: This poem is three – the even lines, the odd lines, and all the lines

Elin ap Hywel

Llwy Garu

Masarnen yw'r pren gorau;
y praffaf. Y mwyaf hydrin,
yn wydn ac ufudd, fel ein cariad ni.

Wrth i'r cŷn lyfu'r graen yn siafins hir
dinoethaf droeon ein gyrfa:

y gannwyll: fflam gyson cariad
sy'n llosgi yn ffenest dywyll nos
y llong: cwch diogel i fforio
y cefnfor tymhestlog rhwng yma a thraw
agoriad fy nghalon, yr allwedd:
fy nhrysorau oll, ti a'u cei.

Mesen, i dyfu yn dderwen o deulu,

Bwydaf di felly
â'm geiriau pren:
llymru o badell ein serch.

Teimla groth y llwy
yn llyfn fel pen baban yng nghledr dy law;
a gwêl sut rwy'n dy garu: dyma'r
dim sydd ym mola'r ddolen
– teimla dy fysedd
yn cau am y ceudod.

Anwylyd, nod y gwir grefftwr
yw gadael gofod rhwng un patrwm a'r llall;
ogof fechan, lle i ti guddio
rhag i ni ddod i ddeall ein gilydd yn rhy dda.

Love Spoon

The best is sycamore:
long-lasting, carvable,
strong yet yielding, like our love.

As the chisel licks long shavings from the wood
I reveal the grain of our future:

a candle: the constant flame of love
burns at night's black window
a ship: our safe vessel crossing
the stormy passage between cradle and grave
the key: to open my heart –
all my treasures I freely give
an acorn: the seed of our oak
our family a canopy of leaves around us

I feed you
with wooden words:
sup from the dish of our passion.

The back of the spoon
is smooth as a baby's head in my palm
and I have remembered to leave
a hint of rough wood in the bowl
life, after all, is no feather mattress.

See how I love you; for here
is the gap at the heart of the handle
let your fingers
close on the nothing.

My love, the true craftsman knows
to leave a space between one thing and another;
a tiny cave, a place to hide
lest we come to know each other only too well.

Latéfa Guémar

Women as Victims of a Rapist State

Since the beginning of the 'dirty war' in 1992, Algerian women have become the most forgotten victims of the brutal Algerian regime and its national and international accomplices. Women have been targeted both by fundamentalist terrorists and by the police. Like their husbands, brothers and fathers, women have been insulted, beaten and dishonoured by both sides of the conflict.

All kinds of violence against women were organised by the iron hand of the different Algerian state institutions. The systematic practice of rape during the dirty war was officially blamed on the 'terrorists'. But the woman's body was also subjected to campaigns orchestrated by the Algerian regime itself. Brutal sexual abuse became standard.

Testimonies, studies and reports on the dirty war have been published by established international organizations, yet further information about this phenomenon remains limited. No details have been made public about the women violated by soldiers. However, it seems clear that, during the dirty war, rape was a banal act practised by both sides, though the Algerian regime was the most active perpetrator of sexual violence. Since the start of the conflict Algerian women have been victims of repression carried out by the various security bodies. Indeed, the 'anti-terrorist fight' took the form of a war against a female population perceived from the very beginning as a tool to be exploited against the enemy.

According to a former army lieutenant now living in exile, in 1993 soldiers were instructed to 'examine' women suspected of being liaison officers in terrorist groups. The instruction was deliberately ambiguous. Suspicions that terrorist Islamists adopted female dress led to deliberately offensive 'inspections'. The Algerian army remains a bastion of male privilege. If they had been serious about examining women appropriately, they would have had to recruit female staff, but this did not happen. The instruction allowed for all women to be considered as potential suspects, and it authorized arrest, examination and the practice of violence against them. These practices ranged from simple frisking to commands to take off hijabs, to remove skirts or trousers, or even more. Soldiers were allowed to use all forms of humiliation. Certain soldiers also had orders to assess the 'piety' of the women under examination. A shaven pubis was considered as a proof of a recent sexual act. Shaven hair became a crime committed by women or a source of information to be exploited by the police.

As military operations progressed into rural areas, Algerian women were increasingly targeted by the police, more and more often insulted, stopped, questioned, violated, raped and tortured. Certain commanders of operational units ordered soldiers, when visiting places supposedly under 'terrorist' influence, to use all forms of violence against women with the aim of procuring information about their husbands' activities. The objective was to destroy the morale of anyone suspected of belonging to the Islamic side.

As with other forms of torture, the intention was to break and dehumanise these women. Those suspected of hiding political rebels or 'terrorist' husbands could be violated with total impunity: this was an acceptable means of undermining rebellion and 'terrorism'. Sadly, only a few testimonies and studies about these facts are available to the general public: these women have been betrayed by the shameful silence of all 'enlightened' and 'civilized' agents, by the 'free press', the intellectuals and the political opposition. And because rape is a crime that is a source of shame for many women, victims are often too ashamed to talk about what is nothing less than torture.

The authorized Algerian official press claims that, between 1997 and 2005, more than 2,000 women were kidnapped, violated and, in the majority of the cases, assassinated by terrorists. The true number of women victims, of both sides, must greatly exceed these official figures. It is only when a national or international independent organisation launches a full enquiry that the truth will be revealed.

During the dirty war, revenge and hatred motivated individuals to practise rape against 'terrorist' wives. By declaring a national amnesty, in 2006, the Algerian state established itself as the protector of 'terrorist rapists'. How horrible! How can one remain silent in the face of such acts, where the majority of rapes were authorized and tolerated, even encouraged, by a morally blind and repressive regime?

It is essential today for us, witnesses or victims of these atrocities who have fled and sought asylum in democratic countries, to use the freedom of expression of our host countries to expose, explain and fight – fight for the victims of this form of torture to be recognised and protected under an international convention. Rights can only be attained through struggle: they will never be donated.

Nedjma X

Speaking Out

I want to tell you about when the immigration officers came to deport me and about when I was raped in my home country. I want to tell you about when I come here for safety. I was suffering mentally and physically in Algeria even before I was raped, and then when I came here I was expecting safety and I was turned away. I expected to be safe, to have empathy.

When I claimed protection I received such a shock from the refusal, from the fact that they didn't believe what I was saying about what had happened to me. Even now I think I will never recover from this....from what I read in the refusal letter. That shock was the biggest shock I received in all my life. All the evidence I gave them from the police in my country but still they didn't believe me. The translator made a mistake with my name and they said to me, 'We don't believe your story because this information wasn't about you.' The translation was very bad.

Even before I was raped the suffering was with my husband. He was beating me, he never cared for the children, he had no responsibility for his family. He was always drinking and taking drugs. And then he started being involved in a strange Berber group and then he disappeared. I didn't know where he was.

I don't want to remember the rape but I want to tell you about it.

Algeria is in a state of emergency. The Home Office says that no woman in Algeria is unsafe, that she can relocate where she wants. But family law in Algeria is horrible. The only thing that woman is good for is sex. We don't have any help... nothing. There has been a state of emergency since 1992. There was an order from the general to rape women to get information about their husbands. They used to come always at night. It happened to many women in Algeria. That day they came during the morning. My daughter was with me. She was three years old. My son was at school.

Two men came... gendarmes. One stayed outside for a while and then they came into my house and went into the kitchen and made a cup of coffee. Because it was a state of emergency they didn't need any papers, they could just come in. I was in the kitchen. When they started to behave as if they are belonging here, as if they are in their own house, then I started to be scared, and I started to fight. I ask them, 'Why are you behaving like as if it is your house?' They said, 'Now we are going to show you how your husband cannot help you. If he is a man ask him to come and help you now.'

They pulled me on the sofa. One raped me. After half an hour I started bleeding. I was shouting and my daughter who was playing came. When she came she saw what was happening and she started shaking. She was in a very bad way. She was very affected. Even now when we came to this country at first she was very scared of men and she used to hide from them.

My son was 5 at that time. He was coming home from school and one neighbour said to my son that the gendarme is in the house. But he was very brave. He came in and when he saw this he started to take care of his sister. And then he noticed the blood.

Then the men left us.

The Home Office believed that I was raped but they said that my husband was political, not me, so I wasn't a refugee. They said, 'Yes, we believe all of this but it wasn't you who did all the political stuff so you can just take steps to go back.' I was scared, shocked, destroyed. I feel like all my life is gone.

They came to deport me. There was an Algerian family that was deported two weeks before so I was very scared and I was sleeping over with my friend because I was very scared.

One day, in the morning, at 7 o'clock they came in my house. I wasn't there so they called me on my phone and said, 'We are the police, we found your door open. If you come back to the house you can show us what has gone so we can help you.'

When I went there I felt something was not right because there isn't any police car. They were hiding. When I came in my home I saw two police and they said, 'Go upstairs to see what is missing.' When I go upstairs nine people came into the sitting room.

One police she said, 'Do you have your passport?' I said, 'No, it's not with me.' So they said, 'We are Immigration,' but I told them I do my Fresh Claim and I showed them the paper and I tell them that I haven't any decision. They say, 'We know.' They said they had to look in my friend's house for my passport. They did a search but they can't find it.

That shocked me and my children. All the time when Immigration are there I'm all crying, crying, crying. And my children were crying, crying, crying. They said I could take them to school but I wanted my children to stay with me. They said that if they carried on crying they would give them an injection to make them stop.

After that they left.

Interview by Heaven Crawley; translation by Latéfa Guémar

Parvin X

My Story

First I came to Swansea alone nobody with me except my husband. When my husband go work I feel so lonely. I sitting by windows all night. I can't see anyone of my country, Bangladeshi people. My husband go shopping because I don't leave the house. I don't know anyone. When I know my neighbour is Bangladeshi then I go to her house and she helped me. My house have no toilet, only outside. In the night I couldn't go to the toilet because I'm so afraid. When my husband came home then I go to the toilet. One room I sitting all night, I couldn't open any other room door.

Two month later I'm pregnant. That time I feel more lonely because I left my whole family, parents and friends then my son born. Nine months, very sick all the time because I can't eat anything except only white rice with salt. Then we went to hospital for delivery time and twenty-four hours delivery pain. First time I haven't any experience and without my mother. My husband, he with me. Forty-eight hour later my son was born. I was vomiting bile, and I was cut bad. After, when they took me in the ward there was more worry to me because I don't speak English. Nobody help me because I don't know anyone. Because it's a hospital and I need to talk then my husband buy a book, language dictionary book, and I read this book and I mark which word I need. Ten days in hospital is awful for me because my son had jaundice. After they find jaundice they put him in a machine and I didn't know why. I cry and cry. I call my husband and he came and he understand what they say and tell me.

In hospital doctor and nurse they helped me all the time. Then I came home after ten days. I had chicken pox and so awful problem because both chicken pox and new baby. The midwife and doctor helped me and my husband. Also my next door neighbour. That was the time I had this friend. Her son help me. Fourteen days after I come home with my baby, her son died in a road accident. Suddenly. He was twelve. He went shopping and he crossed the road and a car came. When I heard he had died I couldn't stay in my house on my own. Awful for me. Also I was afraid because when I go into the kitchen I was seeing his face in my garden. Always in front of me his face.

Two months after my son's birth I found I was pregnant again. This time I feel so unhappy with nobody here. My neighbour was unhappy and she was pregnant too – one week between our daughters. After my daughter born I heard that my grandmother had died. Then I feel more lonely because I remember when I was born my grandmother looked after me more than my mother. And I couldn't go to my country because my husband not let me go. He was awful with me. That started my second life. Because my husband is so, so nasty with me, I couldn't expect he like that. When he married me I didn't know him. Two years later I stay in my house like a prison. No hot water, no central heating, no carpet, no bed, no quilt, no bed covers, only a few blankets. I stay in one bedroom: my kitchen, bedroom, sitting room, dining room is all one room. Everything is one room. I used only calor gas cooker in that room. He sleep in another room. Is awful. Broken bed, he got a bed from a skip where people had thrown it. He not give any food, clothes, only a little. I find carpet in a skip and open it to see if it is nice and take it home in the night and wash it and put it in my room.

The third time I pregnant my son born and same condition continued with my husband. I got five children one by one and continue same with my husband and I never complain to officials. He hit me. If I complain he said he divorce me and also my parents said 'Don't go against him. God help you.' I never go my country since I came here.

In 1999 I start teach Bengali and Arabic in 9 houses. My husband not give us a penny, and there were 3 children in school. Also I work in Singleton Hospital crèche Monday to Friday. Saturday and Sunday – all day teaching. I took my youngest two in a double pushchair; eldest three, he looked after. He took some of that money too

In 2000 doctor find he had a cancer and I help always him, but he blamed me. All the time he blamed me. He told everyone in the community I gave him poison and that made him ill. Nobody believed him and the hospital doctor also not believe him. They know he had cancer. When he was in pain I called the ambulance and I went with him to hospital. When he was better he blamed me again and said I went with him to tell the doctors to give him bad drugs to make him die. My life was awful with him.

Day by day he was ill ill ill. And problems more and more start with the way he was with me. In 2002 he died. 3rd March. He left all mess everywhere: this country and Bangladesh. I went to depression. I started take medicine and that medicine still I take.

I'm happy now. God gave everything now behalf of him. With my five children and I went to Bangladesh after he died in 2002, October. Twelve years without seeing my country. I see my parents and they cry and cry. My grandmother, grandfather I do not see. They died because twelve years is long. In 2002 I started to go Bangladesh and I have been four times now! And my children too. I change completely my house! I buy new bed, wardrobe, washing machine – everything, everything new! New carpets. Television. Before, I have a small one black and white because he doesn't like to pay licence. After he dies, I have eighteen skips – eighteen! – and the house is left only walls. I clear everything away. Twelve black bags I take just out of his bedroom. He collect everything, the basement full rubbish. House with mice. House smelled. I washed and washed. I bought new bath, new bathroom! I paint and wallpaper. The children are so happy. They have everything, everything new. My son he have everything – River Island, Next. I give my children everything they want. Playstation, ipod, laptop. They lucky this mum! Forty-two inch TV – every room TV video – because I like to my children give everything.

My son is seventeen. I am thirty-five. My parents arrange marriage when I was fourteen. I came here I was sixteen. I was second wife. He divorced his first wife because his life is awful with her. Same as with me – he made his life awful. He had lots of money but he made his life awful. Outside everyone know he is good man. He give money to this man, that man. He give to everyone. Not to us. Home start with the family – but not him. We have money – we don't spend anything. He not let me cook except when he say. I cook everything on calor gas. No bills heating, no carpets, no bed, electricity, nothing. When he die, I spend!

Now I have many friends, everyone in my community like me. This is how I am still here. They help me. Every Friday friends come. We have tea, coffee, biscuits, samosas, they say they cannot live without me! We talk, talk, talk. When I go to Bangladesh in the summer, everyone, everyone in Swansea ring me, 'When you come back, when you come back, the road is dead without you.' My children are good. I working now with the community. Quaker house caretaker and cleaner, youth worker, working with children in crèche in WEA.

I want to believe my husband in paradise, not in hell. He is my husband. I try to forgive him but he was very bad with me. But he had awful life. He made his life awful. I think he was ill. I like my house to be clean and tidy and now I make it always clean. Everything new. You come to my house I cook for you. You see how nice it is. I bring samosas next week.

Interview by Jeni Williams

Stevie Davies

Ah

A memoir of the well-meant prohibition on Welsh speaking,
the 1889 Education Act

Now, ah, we are gelding your, ah, tongue.
Don't be alarmed,
it's (say 'Ah!') a routine operation,
easily performed.
We're, ah, doing this for the whole nation.

First we snip the, ah, tongue-string,
there! Ah! Completely painless,
why the fuss?
And the benefit to you is
you get to be, ah ha! one of us.

Now we, ah, slice the, ah, muscle,
so! simple as tonsils,
it won't grow again.
Sew you up, that's it,
shut your bleeding mouth, man, you're done.

Next, ah, please.

Never Speak of Home

He cupped his palms about my ears
to drown the steelworks and the pit.
She turned the BBC up high
spiring her hands above my crib..

May our baby be the best:
may she be well spoken.

Always 'Taf' he was abroad,
wild to spit Wales off his tongue:
but darkly beautiful the brogue
of Tawe lilted through Europe.

Glamorgan the tongue of my tad,
for well-spoken he was.

But hers the soft chalk of Wiltshire
blurring her talk, purring the 'r',
remembering her tribe's
illiterate pauperdom.

And her burr was the heart's melody,
so well-spoken was her.

So I ascended into ether, pure
with the radio-lady's lah-de-dah voice.
I came from nowhere. They had cut
my tongue-string, cast me loose.

May she be superior
and never speak of home.

Zhila Irani

Tears Also Have Something to Say

Scientists have proved that the tears which are caused by chopping an onion, or by gas or smoke getting into the eyes, are chemically different from the tears which we cry because of our emotions. The emotions affect the hormones which produce enzymes which stimulate the glands to produce tears.

When I was little, I remember my mother asking me, 'Do you know what the most important part of the body is?' – 'The ears?' was my first answer. But she told me that without ears you can still live a normal life; many successful people are deaf. Later, my view of the world changed and I thought the answer was the eyes. But she told me, 'No. Blind people can have high levels of perception and lead fulfilling lives.'

When my father passed away, and I was crying on my mother's shoulder, she said, 'Now you have found the most important part of the body. It's the shoulders. They are important because your shoulders can be somebody's refuge for tears, and somebody else's shoulder can be your refuge for tears, and this is very important whenever you are very sad or in pain.'

She wished that I would never be alone and would always have shoulders to cry on. Most friends and acquaintances never see your tears, but the shoulders of a real friend will be wet from your tears.

I now realised that tears also have a place, and something to say, something that we have to discover and understand.

When my mother passed away, I found a shoulder to cry on, but still my tears have something to say! My pain has not been relieved, but rather has accumulated.

When people's freedom is denied, when chains are on their mouths and pens, when expressing oneself is a crime, the most basic requirements for human life don't exist. The only wish one has is to break free from such a despotic situation, even if it is highly unlikely in the near future. In such a situation people will use their tears to draw a picture of their lives, their pain and their wishes. In the vacuum of passion and hope they will find tears a good companion, and the best signal of what cannot be spoken.

The passion and symbolism of speech is like the flow of music. The music of tears is beyond the magic of imagination. We have to know that tears are innate, an international language which none of us needed to learn. Everybody can understand this language, for tears have no geographical borders. Inside each of us, however, tears are the borders between absolute darkness and a spark of hope for life and the future.

All people, in their tears, are searching for what they have lost.

Open your eyes to believe that you are not alone.

Notes on Contributors

Afsaneh Firoozyar was born in Iran, studied Education at university (specialising in children with special needs) and taught for twenty years; she was headmistress of a large primary school for ten years. Since coming to the UK she has learnt English and qualified as a playworker. She makes her living by working in numerous play-schemes and drop-ins, and she also volunteers with the Red Cross and as a classroom assistant in a school for children with special needs.

Aimé Kongolo is from Katanga Province in Congo-Kinshasa and is currently studying at Swansea Metropolitan University.

Amani Omer Bakhiet Elawad was born in Sudan and now lives in Swansea. She is a mother of four. After taking a BSc in Agricultural Economics she went on to a Postgraduate Diploma in Development Planning, then a Masters in Agricultural Economics. While in Sudan she worked in a number of high-level management and research posts, latterly as researcher and deputy manager with the Alfanar Organization for Development and Capacity Building.

Anahita Alikhani studied and tutored in Art at Tehran University, was detained and tortured after working with foreign television crews covering student demonstrations, and fled to the UK in 2001. Besides writing and performing comic monologues, she has made a short documentary film about attitudes to asylum seekers in Wales – titled 'Anonymous' – for Valley and Vale Community Arts.

Angela Hill-Jones has taught at Gors Community School in Swansea for ten years. Born and raised in Glasgow, she married a Welshman and has lived in Carmarthenshire for 23 years. She is interested in environmental issues, film, theatre, music and dance.

Carol Rumens was born in South London. She has worked in Ireland and Sweden, and has recently settled in Wales. She is a Professor of Creative Writing at the University of Bangor. Her new collection of poems, *Blind Spots*, will be published by Seren in April 2008.

Carolyn Edge worked with asylum seekers and refugees in Swansea for four years, has lived in a few different countries and has a passion for trying to make the world a better place.

Catherine Merriman is the author of five novels and three collections of short stories. She also edited *Laughing, Not Laughing* (Honno 2004), a collection of women's autobiographical writing on the subject of sex. Catherine has lived in Wales for thirty-five years.

Dahlian Kirby was born in Billingham, Teeside and moved to Cardiff in 1976 to attend the Royal Welsh College of Music and Drama. She has had plays staged in London, Cardiff and Edinburgh, and has published short stories in several anthologies by Honno and Hafan, in *Planet* and in other magazines. *The Urban Turbans* (Gomer 2007) is a book for children about a Welsh girl joining an Indian Sikh drumming group.

Deborah Kay Davies is the author of the poetry collections *Things You Think I Don't Know* (Parthian 2006) and *Grace, Tamar and Laszlo the Beautiful* (Parthian 2008). She lectures part-time at the University of Glamorgan. Her short stories have appeared in *Mslexia*, on BBC Radio 4, and in anthologies such as *Ghosts of the Old Year* (Parthian) and *Mr Roopratna's Chocolate* (Seren). Her poetry has been published in journals including *New Welsh Review, Poetry Wales, Planet* and *Poetry Digest*.

Elin ap Hywel is a poet working mainly in Welsh. She lives in Aberystwyth, where she is a Royal Literary Fund Writing Fellow at the University of Wales Aberystwyth. Themes of belonging and captivity feature often in her work.

Elizabeth Baines was born in Bridgend and is a playwright, novelist and short-story writer (www.elizabethbaines.com). 'Star Things' features in her collection, *Balancing on the Edge of the World* (Salt 2007). 'Home' is an extract from a novel in progress.

Emily Hinshelwood (cover photograph and 'Sandscape after hours' on page 3) is a poet, playwright and publisher. She lives in Ammanford and is involved in the Hookers' Pen women's writing group and the Peacock Vein Script Shop.

Farzaneh Dadkhah and her daughters **Romisa Asadi** and **Maedeh Asadi** were all born in Tehran. Farzaneh taught in a primary school. She runs a drop-in for Swansea Bay Asylum Seekers Support Group.

Fiona Owen has published the poetry collections *Going Gentle, Imagining the Full Hundred* and *O My Swan*. She also writes and performs music with Gorwel Owen. She teaches for the Open University and occasionally for the Department of Lifelong Learning, Bangor. She is a part-time research student at Bangor, focusing on ecopoetics. 'Autobiography 1' and 'Magda's Song' are from *Going Gentle* (Gomer 2007).

Forough Farrokhzad (1935-1967) is the most famous woman in the history of Persian literature. She published her first poetry volume, *The Captive*, in 1955, following a divorce and the loss of custody of her son. In 1958 she spent nine months in Europe and began her relationship with filmmaker and writer Ebrahim Golestan, who encouraged her love of independence. She published two more volumes, *The Wall* and *The Rebellion*, before going to Tabriz to make a film about leprosy, *The House is Black* (1962), which won awards world-wide. In 1963 she published *Another Birth*: this mature and sophisticated poetry broke profoundly with modern Iranian poetic conventions. Forough died in a car accident, leaving posthumous poems which many consider the greatest of modern Persian literature.

Fridah Kimani came to the UK fleeing violence in Kenya with her mother, in 2002, aged eight. She is at school in Swansea. Her poem 'Through the Eyes of a Window' won a young people's writing prize and has also been published in a magazine for young carers.

Gwyneth Lewis, the first ever National Poet of Wales, composed the words which appear on the facade of the Wales Millennium Centre in Cardiff. She has published six books of poetry in Welsh and English. The first three in English are collected in *Chaotic Angels* (Bloodaxe 2005) and *Tair Mewn Un* (Barddas 2005) collects the first three in Welsh. The BBC made a documentary about *Zero Gravity* (Bloodaxe 1998), a collection inspired by her astronaut cousin's voyage to repair the Hubble Space Telescope. Gwyneth's first non-fiction book, *Sunbathing in the Rain: A Cheerful Book on Depression* (Flamingo 2002), was shortlisted for the Mind Book of the Year. Her second, *Two in a Boat: A Marital Voyage* (Fourth Estate 2005), recounts a voyage she made with her husband on a small boat from Cardiff to North Africa.

Hamira Ageedy is from Mahabad in Iranian Kurdistan. She worked as a GP in Tehran and Mahabad for 17 years. She lives in Swansea with her husband and children. Her stories (others were published in previous Hafan anthologies) are all based on the lives of her former patients.

Heaven Crawley is a researcher and policy analyst. She directs the Centre for Migration Policy Research at Swansea University and is a founder member of the Refugee Women's Legal Group.

Imène Guémar goes to Bishop Vaughan Catholic School in Morriston, Swansea. She was born in Algeria during the 'Dirty War' against civilians. She left Algiers due to her father's persecution by the Algerian regime, when she was at the end of year one. On arriving in the UK she went straight into year 3. Now in year 7, she is in the top group at Creative Writing, Welsh, Art and English.

Ingrid Bousquet was born in France and has lived most of her life abroad: in Cameroon, Gabon and Angola for four years, and for the past seven years in Wales. She is a playworker with the Swansea Bay Asylum Seekers Support Group's Welcome to Play project.

Jackie Aber is a qualified designer and dressmaker who ran her own successful dressmaking business in Gulu town, Uganda. Since coming to the UK she has taken courses including English, IT and childminding. She has qualified as a playworker and completed her Access to Nursing with the long-term aim of becoming a nurse. She has one son.

Janet Dubé was born in Fulham and worked as a schoolteacher and playworker in England. For thirty years she has lived in an ex-farmhouse in North Carmarthenshire, and worked an organic garden with her husband. She was active in the feminist and anti-war movements, and in childrens' playwork. She studied Religions at St. David's University College, Lampeter. She has published prose and poetry, including three slim volumes. She has three adult children and three grandchildren and works for the British Red Cross in Carmarthen.

Jeni Williams teaches Literature and Art History at Trinity College, Carmarthen, and researches the arts and culture of Wales. She was the theatre critic for *New Welsh Review* (1997-2001) and continues to take an interest in innovative performance of all kinds, including new writing. She writes regularly on literature, theatre and art for *New Welsh Review* and *Planet*. She is the general Arts editor for Parthian Books, and contributing editor of *Sideways Glances: Five Off-centre Artists in Wales* (Parthian 2005). She has published poetry in journals including *Poetry Wales*, *Orbis*, *New Welsh Review*, *Planet* and *New Writing*. Her first collection, *Making Lives*, is due out in spring 2009.

Jo Mazelis was born and lives in Swansea. She lived in London from 1979 to 1991, working for radical magazines including *Spare Rib*, *Women's Review* and *City Limits*. Her first collection of short stories, *Diving Girls* (Parthian 2003) was short-listed for Commonwealth Best First Book and

Welsh Book of the Year. Her book *Circle Games* (Parthian 2005) was long-listed for Welsh Book of the Year. She is also a photographer, print-maker and designer.

Kate D'Lima (1957-2008) was born in India and lived in Kent, London and Bristol, before moving further west to Swansea. She was Lecturer in Performing Arts, Writing and Literature in the Department of Adult Continuing Education at Swansea University, and was researching Creative Writing in Health Settings for a PhD. Kate's awards as a writer of fiction included runner-up in the Rhys Davies short story competition 2008. Kate died tragically young in January 2008.

Kimba Cate is from Uganda. Her story ('Forgiveness') tells it all.

Latéfa Guémar was forced to give up her scientific research post and flee Algeria, following attacks on her family as a result of her husband's work as a journalist. Having received refugee status in the UK, she is now taking a part-time degree in Humanities, focusing on race and equality. Latéfa has undertaken research with the Open University on the reporting of security issues and its impacts on Arabic speakers in the UK, and with the Refugee Council (UK) on the implications of anti-terrorism legislation for asylum seekers and refugees. She coordinates the project 'Parenting in a Multicultural European City' in Swansea University. Latéfa is a research associate of the Centre for Migration Policy Research, is active in Swansea Bay Asylum Seekers Support Group, and chairs the Swansea Women's Asylum Support Group.

Liz Morrison is from Brecon. She recently took an MA in Creative Writing at Swansea University. She worked in refugee camps in Croatia and Austria in the 1990s.

Maedeh Asadi was born in Tehran and lives in Swansea where she is taking A-levels in Law, Psychology and Spanish.

Maggie Harris was born in Guyana. Her first collection, *Limbolands*, won The Guyana Prize for Literature 2000. *From Berbice to Broadstairs* was published in 2006. She was granted a bursary from Arts Council South-East for *The Conch Shell*, and is a Kingston University Press prize-winner for her manuscript in progress, titled *Being Caribbean in Carmarthenshire*.

Meryam Fotohe was an excellent sportswoman when young. She and her husband had a successful business in Iran where she devoted herself to supporting her family. She has always worked for charities.

Mona Balbaki was born in a Lebanese family in Sierra Leone. When she was 14 the family moved back to Lebanon. She studied nursery education at university and became a nursery teacher. She is married and has two children. Her husband is Iraqi – and that is why she is here. Since arriving in the UK she has learnt English and IT and qualified as a playworker.

Monika X is from South Africa. She has a son.

Nazand Begikhani was born in Iraqi Kurdistan in 1964 and has lived in exile since 1987: in Denmark, France and later the UK. She holds a PhD in comparative literature from the Sorbonne and has published three poetry collections in Kurdish. A poem from her first collection in English, *Bells of Speech* (Ambit 2007), was nominated for the Forward Poetry Prize. She translates from French and English into Kurdish, e.g. Baudelaire and Eliot. An active researcher and advocate for women's human rights, she is a founding member and co-ordinator of Kurdish Women Action Against Honour Killing. Nazand currently works at BBC Monitoring. Her poem is reprinted with kind permission from Ambit Books.

Nedjma X is from Algeria. She managed to divorce her husband and has now married again and settled in Swansea. She has learnt English and is training to be a playworker.

Parvin X is from Bangladesh. Her story tells it all.

Pascale Petit is a French/Welsh poet living in the UK. She was a co-founding tutor of The Poetry School and co-founder of *Poetry London* where she was Poetry Editor for 15 years. Among her collections, *The Huntress* and *The Zoo Father* were both short-listed for the TS Eliot Prize and were Books of the Year in the *Times Literary Supplement*. Her fourth collection, *The Treekeeper's Tale*, is published by Seren in October 2008.

Perian X is a Kurd from Turkey. Until recently Kurds were violently oppressed in Turkey, denied rights and prohibited from speaking and writing in Kurdish. Although this has eased recently, recent Turkish attacks on Iraqi Kurdistan demonstrate the continuing difficulties Kurds face in the country.

Rhian Saadat was born in south Wales, spent her childhood in Germany and Cyprus, and has worked in the Middle East and Southern Spain. She recently gained an MA in Creative Writing from the

University of East Anglia, and now lives in Paris. Her poetry collection *Window Dressing for Hermes* was published by Parthian in 2004.

Romisa Asadi studied archaeological preservation at Tehran University before leaving Iran. She took an A-level in Art at Swansea College and is now studying Medical Genetics at Swansea University.

Rosemary Jones was born in South Wales and studied Art History at Cambridge. She has had many different jobs, including running a farm in West Wales, managing a T-shirt factory in Nairobi and running a bookshop in Carmarthen. She is a volunteer case-worker and fundraising events organiser with Asylum Justice in Swansea.

Rouhi Downing is an Iranian artist. She has a BA in Art from Carmarthen School of Art, where she was deeply influenced by her tutor, the Welsh artist Mary Lloyd Jones. Rouhi further developed her interest in textiles and combined it with ongoing concerns with gender and culture in a Masters in Anthropology, where she focused on the work of women weavers from a nomadic tribe in Iran. She lives with her British husband in West Wales, where she draws and paints.

Sadhbh O'Dwyer is from Tipperary, Ireland. Before moving to Wales she worked in Ireland, France and Japan. She lives in Swansea with her husband and daughter.

Sherhayar Khalid and **Shazaib Khalid** are aged 12 and 9 respectively. They care for their mother and little sister and still manage to excel in school.

Sylvie Hoffmann was born in France and migrated to Britain in 1973, studying at London University and then taking a PGCE in Swansea. She is a freelance artist, storyteller, teacher and dramatist. Sylvie has two daughters, a BA in Architectural Stained Glass from Swansea Institute, a GCSE in Welsh and a license to fly.

Stevie Davies is a Welsh-born novelist, literary critic, biographer and historian, whose books have won many awards. She is Director of Creative Writing at Swansea University. Her tenth novel, *The Eyrie* (2007), is set in Oystermouth, near Swansea; it features 'Red Dora', a 92-year-old socialist veteran of the Spanish Civil War. Stevie recently returned from Egypt, where she was researching an epic novel, *Into Suez*, set in the 1950s (to be published by Weidenfeld in 2009).

Stevie Krayer has published the poetry volumes *Questioning the Comet* (Gomer 2004), *Voices from a Burning Boat* (U. Salzburg 1997) and *The Book of Hours* by R M Rilke (translation) (U. Salzburg 1995). She co-authored *When the Rain Returns: Toward Justice and Reconciliation in Palestine and Israel* (American Friends Service Committee 2004), *Opening the Door: The Spiritual Hospitality Project Report* (Meeting of Friends in Wales 2003) and *Mae'r Gân yn y Galon: Quakers in Wales Today* (Meeting of Friends in Wales, 1997). 'Beirdd y Mynydd Bach' is from *Questioning the Comet*. 'An Evil Spell' is previously unpublished.

Tiffany Atkinson is a lecturer in English and Writing at the University of Wales, Aberystwyth. Her first poetry collection, *Kink and Particle*, was published by Seren in 2006, and is a Poetry Book Society recommendation.

Tracey Curtis is a singer-songwriter living in Ammanford. She was part of pop punk act Shelley's Children, then her solo career was launched when her children asked her to write a protest song against a planned bypass that would ruin their local riverside play area. 'Where Are They Now' is a song from her first CD, *If the Moon Could Talk* (2004).

Trezza Azzopardi was born in Cardiff and lives in Norwich. She has written three novels: *The Hiding Place* (short-listed for the Booker Prize and winner of the Geoffrey Faber Memorial Prize), *Remember Me* (short-listed for the Welsh Arts Council Book of the Year) and most recently *Winterton Blue*. She also writes short stories and pieces for radio and the press. Her work has been translated into seventeen languages. She currently teaches Creative Writing at the University of East Anglia.

Zhila Irani (a pseudonym) came to the UK from Iran with her husband and children about six years ago, seeking asylum. Since being granted refugee status she has resumed her scientific career, studying in Wales for a Masters and now a PhD. Her article here is based on one she published in a women's magazine in Tehran. Its combination of science, emotion and politics did not please the authorities.

Zoulikha Zaidi is an Algerian mathematician. Dr Zaidi came to the UK in 2003 and was granted refugee status in 2006. She is a single mother of three children. To increase her chances of getting a full-time job in Higher, Further or Adult Education, she is taking a PGCE course. At a very young age, she was struck by the unfair and oppressive way women and children were treated, and she realised that religion was used as a powerful tool to make women accept discriminatory social rules. Alongside her work as a university lecturer in Blida, she was involved in an association helping children and youth, in particular child victims of terrorism in her part of Algeria.

Also from Hafan Books

Gŵyl y Blaidd – Festival of the Wolf

co-published with & distributed by Parthian Books. ISBN 9781905762200

200 pages and 1200 years of writing from Wales by and about refugees, presented in both Welsh and English:

from **Canu Heledd** (Heledd's Songs, c.900 AD) – "Heledd hwyedic ym gelwir..."   "I am called wandering Heledd..."
to **Menna Elfyn** – "Ac ym mhob ffurfafen / mae mudo, cymysgu / â'r ddaear am nodded..."   "And in every firmament / migrators mingle, mixing / heaven and earth for shelter..."
and **Hamira Ageedy** – "...curodd rhywun wrth ei drws..." "...someone knocked on her door..."

www.hafan.org / www.parthianbooks.co.uk

Supporting Organisations

This book has been produced by Swansea-based volunteers with refugee-led organisations and refugee support organisations.

Asylum Justice operates as a division of the Welsh Refugee Council in Cardiff, Newport and Swansea, providing legal advice to those who are seeking or have sought asylum, and have no access to Legal Aid. Professional lawyers give their time, and lay volunteers provide administrative support, research and interpreting. Contact: 07876636673.

Swansea Bay Asylum Seekers Support Group is run jointly by local citizens, refugees and asylum seekers. We provide social and cultural amenities, advice and emotional support. Our core work is funded by Comic Relief. See www.hafan.org or contact: 07736408064.

Swansea Women's Asylum Seekers Support Group runs monthly meetings at Swansea Women's Centre, enables women to access other services (eg by organising childcare), and runs occasional seminars (eg with Swansea University's Centre for Migration Policy Research), highlighting the specific barriers which women asylum seekers face in finding justice and protection. Contact: 07809710175.

The **Welsh Refugee Council** is the main provider of support and advice to refugees and asylum seekers across Wales, especially in the four 'dispersal areas': Cardiff, Newport, Swansea and Wrexham, where asylum seekers are sent by the Home Office to be accommodated while awaiting a decision on their claim. The Welsh Refugee Council can put you in touch with other local support groups. Contact: 029 2048 9800.

The Welsh Refugee Council's **Hardship Fund** provides discretionary cash in emergencies, mainly to the homeless and destitute. When an asylum claim is rejected, with no further right of appeal, the claimant loses all support from public funds. Of course they have no right to work. Many prefer destitution to the prospect of returning; or cannot be returned anyway. See www.welshrefugeecouncil.org/destitution.php.

The WRC's Hardship Fund is among the projects with asylum seekers and refugees in Wales which are supported and/or run by major charities like **Oxfam Cymru** and the **British Red Cross**, whose work is traditionally overseas. Such organisations increasingly deal with the consequences of the UK's punitive and inefficient asylum process.

Refugee Week Wales (in the third week in June) showcases support projects and celebrates solidarity: see www.refugeeweekwales.net.